FROZEN BRITAIN

Ian McCaskill and Paul Hudson

GREAT NORTHERN

IAN McCASKILL

Ian McCaskill was born in Glasgow and educated at Queen's Park School, Glasgow and Glasgow University. National Service took him into the RAF and in 1959, he joined the Meteorological Corps as an Airman Meteorologist based firstly at Kinloss in Scotland, and later at RAF Akrotiri on the island of Cyprus. He left the RAF in 1961 to join the Met Office, being posted to Preswick Airport, Malta as well as to Manchester Weather Centre.

In 1978 he transferred to London Weather Centre and became a member of the BBC's forecasting team in October of that year. Apart from a break between 1983 and 1985 when he worked at Birmingham Airport and as a weatherman for Central Television, he stayed at the BBC until his retirement from the Met Office on 31 July 1998. He is a Fellow of the Royal Meteorological Society.

As a BBC weatherman, Ian was hugely popular for his cheery, sometimes eccentric and always entertaining style. Since retiring from regular weather forecasting duties, he has been a guest on numerous TV programmes, including Masterchef, Style Challenge and Fit Club. His distinctive style has made him the most imitated BBC TV weather forecaster, culminating in the ultimate accolade – his own Spitting Image puppet.

PAUL HUDSON

Before joining BBC Look North, weather presenter Paul Hudson was an international forecaster at the Met Office in Bracknell where he was on hurricane and cyclone watch for places such as Miami, South Australia, the Pacific Islands and Singapore. But Paul believes that dramatic weather is not only found in far off places. He has already produced four best-selling books featuring some of the extreme weather conditions that have occurred over the years in his home patch of Yorkshire, and further afield.

Paul was born and brought up in Keighley, near Bradford, and after gaining a first class honours degree in geophysics and planetary physics at Newcastle University, he joined the Met Office. In 1997 Paul became BBC Yorkshire and Lincolnshire's weather presenter, a job he still has today.

In 2007 Paul left the Met Office to join the BBC, and today splits his time between broadcasting and his new role as climate correspondent. He is author of a successful and highly regarded BBC blog on weather and climate.

Publisher's Note

FROZEN BRITAIN

This book is an eagerly awaited sequel to the best-selling *Frozen in Time*, which caught popular imagination with its evocative portrayal of human hardship in such dreadful winters as 1947, 1963 and 1979.

Published in 2006, its final chapter looked to the future. In the light of subsequent events, it would have been all too easy to make fun of the comment: 'The science of climate change seems to suggest that cold, snowy winters may be a thing of the past.' To do so would have been to miss a second key statement: 'A small but growing minority of scientists believe that global warming may actually lead to very much colder winters.'

These words could scarcely have been more prophetic, for soon after the book was published the UK experienced three successive cold winters, which sent records tumbling. Part One of this new book highlights their severity and includes many memorable photographs. In a key difference from its predecessor, as most newspaper pictures of winters such as 1947 and even 1979 were in black-and-white, here colour photos in these pages capture all the subtleties of winter weather at its most glorious and yet most extreme.

In response to continuing requests, *Frozen Britain* features now classic text that formed the core of *Frozen in Time* – legendary stories, in turn amusing, inspiring, astonishing and downright weird!

The final part again looks ahead, presenting both sides of the argument that has made climate change such a complex and yet fascinating subject. *Frozen Britain* is a rattling good read that also features many remarkable illustrations.

Great Northern Books
PO Box 213, Ilkley, LS29 9WS
www.greatnorthernbooks.co.uk

First published 2006 as Frozen in Time
This updated paperback edition published in 2011

ISBN: 978 1905080 98 4

Design and layout: David Burrill

CIP Data
A catalogue for this book is available from the British Library

CONTENTS

Prologue

Well – what a turn up! We had good reason to expect at least spells of reasonable weather during the winters of 2009/10 and 2010/11. We were practically promised it – and were even looking forward to it! We also had good reason to expect a bit of a break in the perpetual frost and gloom.

But what did we get? Record breaking minima and nearly Scandinavian amounts of snow. A friend of mine, sporting a beautiful sun-tan, had emigrated from one of the more blessed islands of the Indian Ocean to Britain to salvage the dregs of the British winter. I still wake in the night sweating, tossing and turning at the thought that I had practically promised this lady no or at the most, very little snow – only just enough to make the Christmas cards interesting.

I knew I was taking a risk with the snow – always a true gambler's call. A fraction of a degree can make any of us a liar. And, of course, if any snow does fall, it can hang about for days as a mute testimony to our weakness in forecasting snow. I hate it!

Under the stress of the weather, the lady's beautiful sun-tan soon faded to a Procol Harum-esque Whiter Shade of Pale, which just made me feel even worse about luring her away from her Indian Ocean paradise.

Gazing out of my window at the snow evoked memories of long-ago winters, including one of the worst of them all - 1947. I was already interested in the weather and keeping a record of daily temperatures and I can remember the shock when I discovered that the temperature even inside our Glasgow house was well below freezing. We didn't have telly weathermen in those days; we didn't even have telly. The drifting snow was piled up three feet or more deep at the edge of the pavement outside my Scottish home and when you are just eight years old and only three feet tall, it leaves a mark!

My six year-old brother and I had another good reason to remember that winter. This was the era when children were seen but emphatically not heard, were told nothing and knew less, so when my mother wrapped us in our warmest clothes, marched us through the snowy, frozen streets and put us on the tram in south Glasgow we were not told the reason for our journey. The tram rattled slowly through the snow ten miles to Renfrew, where our dear Aunt Ella was waiting to meet us. With a hug and a kiss, but without a word, Mother jumped straight back on the tram and disappeared back the way we had come. Our self-control vanished as we saw the tram receding from us, outlined against the snow. Despite all Aunt Ella's efforts to console us, we clung to each other, sobbing and howling, not knowing why we had been exiled from our home. We stayed in Renfrew for two weeks and only when we were eventually summoned back to Glasgow, did we discover the reason for our exile, as we were greeted by a much slimmer mum nursing our brand new baby sister.

The winter of 1963 was every bit as severe and prolonged as 1947. By then I was grown up and a weather forecaster at RAF Leuchars - I was in shock after coming there from my previous posting to Cyprus. Leuchars was an important base at the time - a "master diversion" airfield, manned by thousands of personnel, that held a vital part of our Cold War defence against possible nuclear attack. However, the phrase "Cold War" took on an entirely new meaning that winter. Leuchars was a forward outpost of fighter aircraft, poised 24/7 to intercept anything hostile approaching from the East. But morning briefings were sad, short affairs that winter, as the prolonged sub-zero temperatures and falls of snow made scrambling anything other than eggs impossible. We even tried taxiing the fighters slowly up and down the runways, gunning their engines, while the jet-wash blasted the surface. The ice melted, but only briefly, and then re-froze into a perfect, 1,000 foot ice-rink. Nothing the wit or muscle of man could devise could free those runways from ice and snow. As fast as one part was cleared, another would freeze and, in a winter where even the sea froze for a hundred yards offshore, using salt to melt the ice proved as ineffective as jet-wash. Nothing at all landed or took off from those runways for six weeks. Had the Soviets chosen to attack during that period, we couldn't have done a thing about it.

The 1978-79 "Winter of Discontent" was another very severe winter and made even worse by the industrial disputes that paralysed the country. I was living on the fringes of the Peak District in Derbyshire at the time and I can remember the snowdrifts lying for weeks on end - some of the North-facing gullies still had snow in them in June, but it wasn't the snow, cold and ice, nor the frozen pipes and blocked roads, nor the endless series of strikes by tanker drivers, road hauliers, hospital workers, dustbin men, gravediggers and, it seemed, just about everybody else, that made that winter so bitter for me. I could have survived all that without complaint, but when the weather caused the local pubs to close because their pipes were frozen and the brewery drays couldn't get through the snow, it was time to give emigration to warmer climes some serious thought!

I now watch the weather forecasts with even greater interest than I did before I retired. The detail and accuracy of the forecasts is even better than in my day... if only the weather was better too!

Ian McCaskill

Runways blocked by snow caused many flights to be cancelled.

The battle to keep open the M1 is here being won but was not always successful.

PART I

Double Trouble: Two Severe Winters

Winter 2009-10

If we Britons have learned one thing from the debate about climate change, it's that the world has been getting warmer over the past few decades. For proof of that we only had to look at the great British winter. For over twenty years we'd been enjoying - if that's really the right word - mild winters and ever earlier springs. So sparse had been the winter frosts and snows that many of the current generation of university students have never been sledging more than once or twice in their entire lives.

However, Mother Nature never ceases to find ways to surprise us and, no sooner had we all come to accept the old men's lament that "we just don't get winters like we used to anymore", that we were blitzed by some of the worst winter weather that any generation has had to suffer.

The steam locomotive 'Tornado', which was able to take 100 passengers on a train from London Victoria to Ashford when all Eurostar services were cancelled.

Cynics, perhaps unfairly, began preparing for a harsh winter in 2009-10 as soon as the Met Office published its long-range forecast in October, predicting a mild winter. That followed its earlier notorious prediction of a "barbecue summer", which in fact produced near-constant rainfall and the wettest July for almost 100 years.

Snow did not begin falling until mid-December but it soon made up for lost time. A light snowfall on 16 December was followed by very heavy overnight snow the next day, causing widespread disruption all the way up the eastern half of England from Kent to North Yorkshire. Several deaths were attributed to the effects of the weather.

During the night of 18–19 December, four Eurostar trains broke down inside the Channel Tunnel after leaving France, and another broke down in Kent, as the trains suffered electrical failures because of freezing overnight temperatures. Although the trains had been "winterised", the systems could not cope with the conditions. The cause of the breakdowns was not immediately clear, but Eurostar spokesmen blamed the sudden contrast between the below-freezing temperatures above ground and the 25°C (77°F) heat of the tunnel, affecting the high-speed engines.

More than 2,000 hapless passengers were trapped aboard the broken-down trains for up to sixteen hours, without heating, lighting and air-conditioning, and food and water rapidly ran out. Some passengers were evacuated via service tunnels to car trains, but others were forced to stay on their trains until they could be towed out of the tunnel. Eurostar laid on special services on the evening of 19 December to transport "vulnerable passengers" between London and Paris and Brussels, but a train from Paris then became the sixth train to break down after becoming stuck near Ebbsfleet, Kent.

Another 75,000 would-be passengers then had their travel plans disrupted, as all Eurostar services were cancelled from Saturday 19 December to Monday 21 December, although about 100 people were able to make the journey from London Victoria Station to Ashford International railway station courtesy of some rather less modern, but apparently more reliable old-style technology: a steam train hauled by "Tornado". An independent review of the chaos on the Eurostar services, published on 12 February 2010, made scathing criticisms of the inadequate contingency plans that had been put in place by Eurostar to assist passengers stranded by delays.

The snow on 18-19 December also caused widespread transport disruption across great swathes of England, Wales, Scotland and Ireland. Many airports were closed and the M25 and large parts of the M3, M4, M40, M1 and M11 motorways in England were brought to a standstill until late into the night, and many towns were gridlocked. Large numbers of schools were also closed the next day.

After a brief lull, fresh overnight snowfall on 22 December brought further problems in the UK, with Hampshire and the Thames Valley particularly badly hit. Southampton Airport cancelled or diverted all inbound and outbound flights for several hours because the runways were frozen and train services from Southampton Airport Parkway were cancelled. In Basingstoke some 3,000 motorists were forced to either abandon their vehicles or sleep in them overnight after becoming stuck in gridlocked traffic and a total of 2,000 cars were abandoned. The AA accused some local authorities of not acting quickly enough to grit roads and claimed some key roads had not been treated at all. The Local Government Association at once issued a counter-blast, dismissing the claims as "unverified, unsubstantiated and unjustified".

That night the temperatures once again dropped to well below freezing, with Dalwhinnie in the central Highlands of Scotland recording a low of -16°C (3.2 °F). Even in Edinburgh the temperature fell to -10°C (14.0 °F), causing Scottish Transport Minister Stewart Stevenson to state that conditions on Scottish roads were the worst for twenty years. At Prestwick Airport a Ryanair flight overshot the runway on landing after skidding on ice, though no injuries were reported. At the other end of Britain two women were killed and more than forty people injured following a coach crash on an ungritted country road in Cornwall as a party returned from a trip to see the Christmas lights in Mousehole.

The bitter weather extended right across Northern Europe. Three people were found dead from hypothermia in Sarajevo and Teslic in Bosnia and Herzegovina, and police in Poland reported that fifteen people had frozen to death in a single night as overnight temperatures plummeted to -20°C (-4°F), and that overall, forty-seven people had died as a result of the cold during the month. Appeals were made to Poles to report any homeless or drunk people lying outdoors in an attempt to reduce the number of deaths from exposure. Meanwhile, heavy snow in Saint Petersburg, Russia, beginning on Christmas Eve and continuing until Boxing Day, covered the city with the deepest December snowfall seen there since 1881.

On Christmas Day, parts of Britain had a white Christmas for the first time since 2004 after snow fell in Scotland and across England as far south as Nottinghamshire. A man in Leeds, West Yorkshire, froze to death after spending twenty-four hours trapped in his car. He was one of twenty-one people reported to have died as a direct result of the cold snap

On 29 December UK temperatures dropped again, falling to -18°C (-0°F) in parts of the Highlands, with Braemar recording Britain's lowest temperature of the winter so far, and the following day, the Sportscotland Avalanche Information Service (SAIS) issued warnings about dangerous accumulations of snow and ice on Scottish mountains. However, despite the warnings, three people perished after avalanches were triggered. Two climbers were killed as a result of an avalanche on Ben Nevis, and another man who had been airlifted to hospital after getting into difficulties on a mountain in Torridon, Wester Ross, died of his injuries and hypothermia.

The death toll from the cold snap kept rising. In addition to the three people killed in the Scottish avalanches, three more died in a car crash on the M62 near Huddersfield after their car skidded on the snow-covered carriageway and crashed into the barriers. Three other bodies were recovered from frozen ponds. A woman drowned after her car skidded into a pond near Bristol and two wildfowl hunters drowned after trying to rescue their Labrador from a freezing lake in Northamptonshire. They had been shooting geese at Brightwell Lake, near Ringstead, when the accident happened. They were reported missing on 22 December, and the body of one victim was found soon afterwards, but with minimal hope of finding the other man alive, the search was called off over Christmas because the sub-zero temperatures made the ice-covered lake too perilous for police divers. After the weather eased a little, they eventually found the body of the other man on 30 December.

Despite warnings to drivers in many parts of the country, including Northumberland, Cumbria and the Scottish Highlands, not to travel unless absolutely necessary, the New Year celebrations were mostly unaffected by the weather. Police in Edinburgh and Glasgow urged people not to underestimate the dangers of heavy drinking in icy weather. "Have a plan for getting home and stick to it," Chief Superintendent Bernard Higgins of Strathclyde police, said. However Scottish revellers largely ignored the warnings, braving temperatures of -6°C

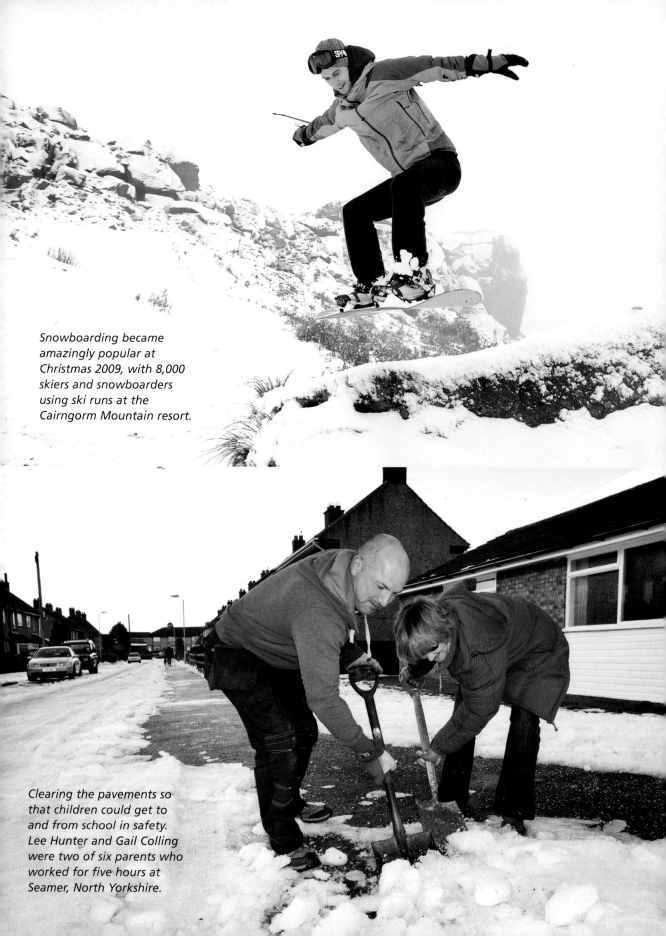

Snowboarding became amazingly popular at Christmas 2009, with 8,000 skiers and snowboarders using ski runs at the Cairngorm Mountain resort.

Clearing the pavements so that children could get to and from school in safety. Lee Hunter and Gail Colling were two of six parents who worked for five hours at Seamer, North Yorkshire.

Typical scene on the many roads clogged by traffic jams and abandoned cars.

to celebrate Hogmanay in traditional style. Only the celebrations in Inverness, including a street party and open air concert, were cancelled because of the cold, amid concerns over public safety, and for the second time that week Inverness Airport was closed, disrupting the travel plans of several hundred passengers. New Year celebrations in other parts of Scotland largely went ahead as planned despite fresh snowfall during the afternoon and evening, though Edinburgh's Hogmanay celebrations were briefly affected when police had to evacuate revellers from one part of the Royal Mile after heavy winds blew large plumes of sparks from braziers into the crowds

Elsewhere there were mixed fortunes for New Year revellers. Some thirty intrepid members of the Leeds University Cross Country Club had arranged to hold their New Year's Eve party at the Tan Hill Inn - at 1732 feet, the highest pub in Britain. They set out on New Year's Eve but many of them had to abandon their cars on the A66 - the notorious winter blackspot, Stainmore Pass - as the weather worsened. Undeterred they battled their way through the snow to the pub but the celebrations then went on rather longer than planned - seventy-two hours - after they ended up living the drunkard's dream: snowed in at the pub, surrounded by seven foot snowdrifts.

Student Nathan Martin, 26, from Huddersfield, said: "We were meant to have a barn dance, but it was too cold in the barn so we stayed in the pub. Despite not being able to get out, we've had a good time. There are about thirty of us in total in the pub, and we've all been mucking in helping with chores like washing up and there's been a pub quiz every night which has helped to keep us going. It's been fun, it's like the ultimate lock-in really. We were meant to be leaving on New Year's Day, but luckily we're not really in a rush to go home." They were finally able to head for home - no doubt with suitably painful hangovers - after snowploughs broke through on 3 January

A Scottish woman who lived with her husband in one of the most remote places in Great Britain - the lighthouse keeper's cottage at Cape Wrath, Sutherland, on the north-west tip of Scotland - had an even longer wait to get through the snow. Kay Ure, 54, left her house and the clifftop cafe she runs with her husband, John, to go to Inverness on an organised shopping trip on 19 December. Her husband drove her the eleven miles to a jetty where their boat was moored and from there they crossed the Kyle of Durness where she was picked up by a minibus. She did her shopping, including a turkey for their Christmas dinner, but on her return to Durness, the heavy snow had blocked the route to the lighthouse and Mr Ure, 57, was unable to make the drive to pick her up.

On 4 January newspapers were reporting that she still hadn't made it home again after being cut off by heavy snow for fifteen days. She was stranded in Durness, sitting out the storms in a friend's caravan, and separated by eleven miles of snow-blocked roads from her home and her husband. Mr Ure spent Christmas Day alone apart from their six Springer Spaniels and two walkers who had braved the snow to reach the cafe. The Ures had spoken on the telephone each night and although their Christmas presents remained unopened, the turkey was still in good condition, frozen by nature's deep-freeze. Mrs Ure still hadn't abandoned the idea of sharing Christmas dinner with her partner of more than thirty years, though she thought it would be "a few days yet as the road from our home is dangerous. Part of it is known as the "Wall of Death" so I don't want John attempting it until it's clear. I'm looking forward to a belated Christmas dinner but it might be Burns' Night (25 January) before I get to eat it."

The continued freezing temperatures were far from bad news for all Scots. The Cairngorm Mountain ski resort reported its best Christmas holiday season for fourteen years. After heavy snowfall on the mountains, the four-day period following Christmas Day saw more than 8,000 skiers and snowboarders using the resort's ski-runs. Over the month as a whole, 15,000 skiers had been on the slopes, almost eight times as many as in the comparable period the previous year.

While the snow and freezing temperatures made skiers happy, it was a very unhappy new year for 400 householders in West Yorkshire. Burst pipes on New Year's Eve saw 2,500 gallons of water leak into the local gas network, leaving 400 homes in Dewsbury and Batley without gas during the sub-zero temperatures. The last homes were not reconnected to the gas supply until a week later, 7 January.

As the old year ended, Matt Dobson, forecaster for MeteoGroup, the Press Association's weather division, said it had been the coldest December for thirteen years, though it could have been even worse. "The second half of the month was very cold indeed but the first half was relatively mild," Dobson said. "If it had been colder in the first few weeks we would have seen more records broken." Met Office forecasters added that the cold snap was already the longest since 1981, and warned that "there is no end in sight." Much of the UK was again blanketed in heavy snow as the extreme weather headed south and forecasters added the further gloomy prediction that Britain was on course for its coldest winter in thirty years.

Just as the forecasters had predicted, the New Year brought no let up in the icy conditions, with the Met Office issuing ten extreme weather warnings on New Year's Day alone, and the predicted heavy snow duly arriving in northern England and Scotland. On 4 January, millions of commuters endured a cold and miserable return to work after the holiday break when overnight temperatures plunged to -12°C in some parts of the country. The Federation of Small Businesses estimated that one in ten employees had not made it into work after the holiday break with the weather for once more to blame than post-New Year hangovers. Insurance company RSA predicted that the absenteeism and disruption to production caused by the snow would cost the UK economy around £690m a day.

Motoring organisations had already dubbed 4 January "Black Monday" in anticipation of being called out to a record number of breakdowns in a single day. The AA said it was receiving 4,000 call-outs an hour in the morning and expected to attend more than 22,000 breakdowns by the end of the day, making it the busiest day for more than ten years. The end of the festive break was marred by a series of accidents on the roads, while signal failures and over-running engineering works caused chaos on the rail networks.

In Scotland, Fife Council became the first local authority to confirm that its supplies of road grit were exhausted after it received less than it had ordered from suppliers. Ministers denied there was a shortage of grit and salt and insisted there were "very substantial" supplies for Scotland's roads.

There was one brief glimpse of spring cheer among the midwinter gloom: in Devon gardeners were celebrating after the first daffodils of spring appeared a month earlier than usual. Native British daffodils traditionally start blooming in February, but the changing climate meant they had started appearing much earlier than usual and despite the cold winter, dozens of daffodils in flower had already been spotted in Brixham, Devon.

On 5 January the Met Office issued extreme weather warnings for every region in the UK except the Northern Isles and also warned that temperatures in the Highlands of Scotland

Dwindling supplies of salt limited gritting to major roads, where conditions were nevertheless described as a 'nightmare'.

A postlady struggles through blizzard conditions to maintain deliveries – and with her bike arguably finds it easier than does a road tanker.

Record demand saw power stations struggling to maintain output in January 2010.

could drop to -20°C (-4°F) later in the week. A local record of 48 centimetres (19 inches) of snow was lying in Aviemore and three to four feet (0.91 to 1.2 metres) of snow was recorded within the Cairngorms National Park.

Due to the shortage of road grit – conventionally made from rock salt – some councils were experimenting with grit made from low-grade cooking-type salt mixed with builders' sand, and the public bought up huge amounts of cooking and table salt from shops and supermarkets to spread on their paths and drives.

On Wednesday 6 January about 9,000 schools were shut across England, with 950 in Wales, and at least 250 in Scotland and 16 in Northern Ireland. Peter Hennessy, a history professor at Queen Mary University of London, claimed that the unusually large number of school closures indicated the UK had become a "health and safety nation", though he conceded that, whereas in the past most people would have walked to school, most parents and staff now drove to school, ensuring that snow-bound roads had a far greater impact.

Thousands of homes across the UK were affected by power cuts, caused when power lines either snapped under the weight of ice encrusting them, or were brought down by falling trees. Road and rail travel was severely disrupted by ice and snow, and air travel was almost paralysed by the spate of delays and cancellations. Further deaths caused by the cold were reported in Wales, Shetland and Aberdeenshire.

Hawick and most of the southern Scottish Borders were cut off from the rest of the country for two days, and roads in the south-east of England were clogged by traffic jams and abandoned cars. A spokesman for the prime minister said the government was doing all it could to help councils struggling to cope with the unexpected cold spell, but the freezing temperatures and icy roads were creating "nightmare" road conditions, with many councils hampered by dwindling supplies of salt, limiting gritting to major roads. Even that proved impossible in Perth, central Scotland, when a fleet of gritters was grounded altogether because of the extreme cold, leaving all roads untreated despite temperatures of minus 10 degrees. Perth and Kinross Council said the gritters were unable to leave the depot after the extreme weather led to difficulties in refuelling them with diesel. Perth resident Ian Thomson complained: "I've heard of the rail companies blaming the wrong kind of snow and leaves on the line for disruption but for the council to say it was too cold to get the gritters out is just ridiculous."

Emergency deliveries of road salt and grit were made to councils in Cumbria and Fife after the Government reallocated reserve supplies from Oxfordshire and Buckinghamshire, but stockpiles of salt in other council depots right across the country were running low, though a Local Government Association spokesman insisted that the councils were coping: "As far as we are aware, there are sufficient supplies of salt in the country to deal with the current cold snap. How much grit each council holds depends on local circumstances and how much bad weather they tend to get."

The Winsford rock salt mine in Cheshire had made substantial pre-winter deliveries to the council depots, but was now unable to meet the unprecedented demand for more. "The worst continuous spell of severe weather for twenty years has led to a massive additional demand" a spokesman said. "We would obviously like to be able to fulfil every authority's needs in full, but the reality of the situation at present is that that is simply not possible." The mine had a weekly maximum output of 30,000 tonnes of rock salt, and local councils in England alone were spreading that amount on the roads every single day in an attempt to keep traffic flowing.

On 7 January temperatures of -18°C (0°F) were recorded at Benson, Oxfordshire and Woodford, Greater Manchester, while at Loch Glascarnoch in Scotland the temperature never rose above -8.5°C all day. Over 10,000 schools were now closed across the UK because of the heavy snow and the disruptions to transport. As householders turned up the heating to combat the cold, the National Grid issued two gas alerts in three days, asking suppliers to provide more gas and some businesses to switch to other power sources, as demand hit a new record peak of 454 million cubic metres. Factories were facing gas rationing as supplies dropped and demand surged but, although the Confederation of British Industry warned that the cold weather was causing "massive disruption" for companies, a spokesman did concede that the spread of internet broadband had made it much easier for people to work from home than in previous hard winters. The National Grid issued a rare warning to power suppliers to use less gas after a 30% rise on normal seasonal demand. It has urged power firms to switch to coal, and order more gas supplies from Belgium and Norway. The business secretary, Lord Mandelson, told the BBC it was "a time of special pressure on the grid" but did not comment on claims from the Conservative opposition that Britain had only eight days' worth of gas supplies left.

On 8 January, overnight temperatures fell to -22.3°C (-8.1°F) at Altnaharra, in the Scottish

Highlands about 50 miles south-west of John o'Groats – the lowest UK minimum temperature in fifteen years. Keepers at Knowsley Safari Park near St Helens were feeding their baboons hot baked potatoes in an effort to help the animals keep warm in the bitter temperatures. Said Park Manager David Ross: "In these conditions the baboons absolutely love a baked potato and it's been fantastic to watch adults and youngsters alike collecting the steaming spuds from the keepers and enjoying something warm in the snow."

Overnight snow left Deal and Sandwich in Kent virtually cut off by drifts. That weekend's programme of race meetings, football and rugby matches was badly disrupted by snow and ice, with all but seven games (two in both the Premier League and League 1 and three in the Championship) postponed, though that paled in comparison with the chaos in 1963, when the third round of the FA Cup alone took a total of 66 days to complete.

On 12 to 13 January, as a milder weather system pushing in from the Atlantic came into conflict with the frigid air stationary over Britain, heavy snowfall resumed across the country, with substantial fresh accumulations of up to fifteen centimetres (six inches), on top of the existing lying snow.

In Sheffield, Rotherham, Holmfirth, Barnsley and other areas of South Yorkshire, an "ice storm" of freezing rain or sleet falling onto deep-frozen roads, created so much black ice that some people found that the only safe way to move about on the roads and pavements was by crawling on their hands and knees. Hospital accident and emergency units in Sheffield, Rotherham and Barnsley were inundated by people with fractures and sprains after slipping on what one Sheffield Council official described as "the worst black ice seen in the area in living memory".

Many schools were again closed across England and Wales. There were many road closures and accidents, with the M25 motorway down to one lane between Leatherhead and Reigate, and roads right across the South and the Midlands left untreated, causing havoc for commuters. Gatwick and Birmingham Airports were closed and many flights were delayed at Heathrow.

The weather eased for a while after that, but any thoughts that winter was over were very premature. On 26 February 2010 Glencoe experienced the heaviest snowfalls of any winter sports area monitored by the Ski Club of Great Britain. The owner of the ski resort at Glencoe, Andy Meldrum, said that the ski club reported that eighty centimetres (thirty one and a half inches) of snow had fallen up to the morning of 25 February. "We had thirty-six hours of very heavy snow, so at least two metres must have fallen at the top of the mountain". British skiers and snowboarders opting to spend the winter at home in the hope of good snow conditions on the Scottish mountains, had endured years of sparse or even non-existent snow, coupled with taunts from their jet-setting peers, but the winter of 2009-10 had at last given them something to smile about. The late February storm was the last significant snowfall of the winter, but overall the snow had started earlier, fallen heavier and lasted longer. The UK winter also had one last vicious sting in the tail. Between 29 March and 1 April a huge snowstorm swept northwards over the country and severe blizzards, heavy rain, gale force winds, and severe drifting hammered Scotland and Northern Ireland. Gusts up to eighty miles an hour brought down trees and created waves up to six metres (twenty feet) high. A girl was killed in Lanarkshire when a school bus skidded on ice and crashed. Caravans at Kingshorn were destroyed and a marina in the Lothians was demolished by a powerful storm surge. A seal at St. Andrews Sea Life Centre was swept away by the waves, and a river

Impossible conditions in the Peak District force a lorry driver to give up the struggle and start a long drive in reverse.

True northern grit as groundsman Keith Johnson attempts to clear snow for a Rugby Union match at Harrogate. The event was one of many that had to be cancelled.

Highland cattle are among the hardiest, but still faced gruelling conditions in a winter that decimated farm livestock.

in Musselburgh burst its banks. There were accumulations of up to sixty centimetres (two feet) of snow across Northern Ireland and Scotland and almost a metre (three feet) of snow fell on Aviemore as the winds created enormous snowdrifts. Over 70,000 homes in Northern Ireland and Scotland were left without power and hundreds of new-born lambs perished in the snow at farms throughout Northern Ireland and Scotland. In the North of England, one section of the A635 across the Pennines had remained closed for just under two months, achieving the unwelcome record of being the longest ever road closure in the UK.

When the Met Office published its provisional figures for the UK winter, they revealed that it had been the coldest in thirty-one years. The mean UK temperature was 1.5°C, the lowest since the average of 1.2°C during the 1978/79 winter. Britons were not the only sufferers from the ice and snow, for the 2009-10 "Big Freeze" had extended right across Europe, with several countries experiencing heavy snowfall and record low temperatures, leading to widespread transport disruption and power failures, and a higher number of deaths than for years. The intense cold even spread to parts of the continent that were normally immune to the worst of the winter weather. Heavy snowfall in Spain on 8 March left 220,000 people in and around the Catalonian city of Girona without electricity following a fault with a high tension power cable. The snow blocked railway lines and roads, and Spain's border crossing with France at La Junquera was closed. The snow was reported to be the worst in the region for twenty-five years, while Barcelona had its heaviest snowfall since 1962. The storm even dumped snow on Mallorca and the Balearic Islands and the storms produced waves reaching almost eight metres (twenty-five feet) in the Mediterranean and winds of 133 kilometres per hour (eighty-three mph).

Winter 2010-11

Early in the autumn of 2010, some Polish meteorologists began predicting that the coming winter would be the coldest in Europe in a thousand years. Citing the lower flow speed of the Gulf Stream, resulting in less warm water and less warm air being carried to Europe, they forecast that temperatures during January and February would fall as low as -30°C across much of Europe, and remain there for weeks on end.

The sharp frosts that were then recorded in Britain on 16 October, two weeks before the official end of British Summer Time, suggested that the Polish meteorologists might have been on to something. There were further ominous signs on 22 November 2010, when a cold northerly wind brought snowstorms to northern and eastern parts of Britain that were heavy enough to cause traffic disruption. It was the earliest winter snowfall in the United Kingdom in seventeen years and temperatures were significantly lower than previous November lows.

Eighteen centimetres (seven inches) of snowfall was recorded in Edinburgh, causing chaos on the roads and closing the city's airport. 3,000 homes in the Tayside and Perth areas were left without electricity after the weight of snow and ice brought power lines down, and there was gridlock on the roads in Aberdeen during the evening rush hour of 24 November.

At Redesdale Camp in Northumberland there were several inches of snow on the night of 25 November and a minimum temperature of -9.1°C (16°F). Similar snowfall and low temperatures were recorded all the way from Durham to Aberdeenshire. The following night was even colder with the Welsh towns of Sennybridge and Trawscoed among the most frigid places at -10.2°C (14°F), and Inverness in the Scottish Highlands recording a night time low of -13°C (8.6°F). Even its daytime maximum temperature rose no higher than 0°C. The Met Office then issued severe weather warnings for almost every part of the UK. Sharp frosts and heavy snowfall resulted in widespread school closures, particularly in Northern Scotland, North East England and parts of Yorkshire, but significant snowfalls were also recorded across Staffordshire and the Black Country and in the following days, the snow covered the country, leading to widespread travel disruption, school closures and cancellation of sporting fixtures.

The Republic of Ireland was also badly hit by snow and ice. Barely had the Irish Insurance Federation revealed that the previous winter had cost them a record €297m in insurance pay-outs on 22,450 claims for snow or ice damage to homes, than more winter storms paralysed the country. On Saturday 27 November, snow and freezing temperatures turned many roads in the Dublin area into skating rinks. The prolonged freeze disrupted businesses and schools, made road travel a lottery and caused the cancellation of scores of long-distance and commuter train services, while the main runway at Dublin Airport remained closed for most of the day because of snow and ice.

Back in the UK, the rare phenomenon of "thundersnow" - heavy snow accompanied by thunder and lightning - fell in Dundee, Perth, Aberdeen and Inverness on 28 November. The following night a minimum temperature of -16.1°C was recorded at Altnaharra in the Scottish Highlands, while at the weather station at RAF Linton-on-Ouse in North Yorkshire the temperature fell to -11.2°C - a record low for November. Three weeks earlier, it had also set a record maximum temperature for November of 17.6°C - a spread of almost 29°C in the same month.

The cold brought traffic chaos everywhere, with a spokesman for the Automobile Association describing 29 November as one of the busiest days in the organisation's entire 105 year history as they answered more than 2,100 emergency calls an hour from broken down or stranded motorists right across the country.

Most of the United Kingdom and much of Ireland was covered by snow, with accumulations in the North and East of Scotland and North-Eastern England of over fifty centimetres in places, and over one metre of snow lying on much of the Scottish mountains. For the second year in a row, the previously hard-pressed owners of Scotland's ski resorts were rubbing their hands at the prospect of another bumper season.

On 1 December the M1 motorway was temporarily closed, the Forth Road Bridge was shut for over ten hours after a heavy snowfall, and Gatwick and Edinburgh Airports were closed all day. The trans-Pennine A57 road is a regular casualty of the winter weather, but that evening, snow even blocked the low-lying section between Anston and Worksop and left over 100 motorists stranded overnight. Thousands of motorists across Sheffield were also stranded for a week, beginning on 1 December, after as much as two feet of snow fell on the city. There was severe disruption right across South Yorkshire including the suspension of all bus services for 24 hours.

By now the Met Office was already announcing that it had been the most widespread

Conditions at the end of November 2010 resulted in widespread school closures. These two children are snowballing, while wondering if the school bus will arrive!

Weather observer Geoff Hickling braves the elements on 3 December 2010 to view instruments at RAF Leeming weather centre. It was the day a record low of -17.9° was recorded.

The faces say it all on the first day of December, with passengers huddled on Halifax station platform as they try to cope with transport chaos.

snowfall in the United Kingdom for seventeen years, and it soon became even worse. The South of England had escaped the very worst of the November weather but on the night of 1/2 December, an extremely heavy and prolonged fall of snow hit Southern England. Beginning at around eight in the evening, it had blanketed the South and South-East by daybreak the following morning, with the South Coast particularly badly hit. There were thirty to forty centimetres (twelve to sixteen inches) of snow across East and West Sussex and the South Downs received closer to sixty centimetres (two feet).

The temperatures across the country had reached record lows in November and the early part of December. The Welsh village of Hawarden recorded its coldest November temperature since 1944 with a reading of -9°C (15.8°F) on 27 November but that was dwarfed the following night, when the temperature plummeted to -17.3°C (1°F) at Llysdinam, near Llandrindod Wells in Powys, the coldest November temperature recorded anywhere in Britain since 1985 and the lowest November figure ever recorded in Wales. Northern Ireland also set a new record low for the month when the temperature at Lough Fea fell to -9.5°C (15°F) and Scotland also broke records for November with a night-time low of -15°C (5°F) at Loch Glascarnoch. At Shawbury, in Shropshire the mercury fell to -12.5°C (9°F) and Church Fenton in North Yorkshire was only marginally warmer at -11.9°C (11°F).

On 2 December, Aberdeen recorded a low of -18°C and the temperature fell to -17.9°C at RAF Leeming in North Yorkshire - the lowest temperature ever recorded there since they began keeping records in 1945. Not far away, Topcliffe got in on the record-breaking act with a night temperature of -19.0°C (8F), making it the coldest night since modern records began in Yorkshire, though it was even worse at the perennially cold spot of Altnaharra in the Scottish Highlands. At 10 a.m. on 2 December the temperature was a bone-freezing -21.2°C (-6.2°F), and Braemar and Kinbrace both dropped to -20°C that night.

For some people, the cold brought more than just the misery of burst pipes and disrupted travel. Police and emergency services received huge numbers of calls, including a very seasonal complaint from one irate householder, reporting the theft of his snowman from his front garden. Far more seriously, there were also a large number of deaths as a direct result of the cold. A succession of deaths were caused by people losing control of their cars on snow and ice. A seventeen year-old boy from Bilsington, Kent, was killed when his car left the road; in Glasgow, two pedestrians died after being hit by a Range Rover; a woman in her sixties was killed in a three-vehicle crash in Huntly, Aberdeenshire; and a Sussex man in his early thirties suffered a double disaster. He sustained life-threatening injuries when his Mini was in a crash with a Council Highways Department vehicle near Eastbourne, East Sussex, and then died after a second crash when the ambulance carrying him, being driven by a police officer, slid off the road and crashed on Standard Hill in Ninfield.

Other deaths caused by the cold included a man found dead in the street in Newport, South Wales. It was believed that he had frozen to death after collapsing with a heart attack. Two old-age pensioners were found dead from hypothermia in their snow-covered gardens; a 70 year old man was found dead in the snow in a caravan park in Cleethorpes, and another man from Darlington, County Durham, died while trying to clear snow from outside his home.

As the weather tightened its grip there were yet more deaths. A thirty-three year-old man died when he fell through the ice on the frozen Doggett's Lake in Rochford, Essex; two teenagers were killed after their car skidded on an icy road in Liverpool and crashed into a garden wall; a thirty-five year-old woman and her son, aged nine, were killed in another car crash caused by ice and snow near Castlebellingham in County Louth, Ireland; a fifteen year-old girl died in a sledging accident in Douglas, County Cork in Ireland; and a forty-eight year old man died from hypothermia after sleeping rough in the Bible Gardens, behind Bangor Cathedral, North Wales.

On 6 December, central Scotland suffered a fresh blizzard and further disruption, with many cars and lorries trapped overnight on the M8, and more than 1,000 vehicles stuck on the M876. The M8 remained closed for two days and the resulting political furore forced the resignation of the Scottish Minister for Transport, Stewart Stevenson.

On 9 December, there was a lull in the storms and milder north-westerly winds began to thaw the accumulated snow and ice, but it proved a brief respite from the cold snap, because winter returned with a bang a week later. There was more heavy snow in Southern England beginning on 17 December, with parts of Oxfordshire and Greater London reporting nearly twenty centimetres (eight inches). Snow even settled in Central London, causing severe travel disruption to the roads, the Underground and railways and the airports. Several airports, including London Heathrow were closed while snow and ice was cleared from the runways, leading to long delays. On one of the busiest Christmas shopping days of the season, Brent Cross Shopping Centre was closed. Overnight, temperatures plunged to as low as -8°C in parts of South East England and Greater London.

The next day, 18 December, the band of heavy snow spread to the West Midlands, with up to six inches of lying snow covering an area including Gloucestershire, Warwickshire, Worcestershire and Shropshire and twenty centimetres - eight inches - reported on higher ground south of Birmingham. The M5 was gridlocked, and a number of coach passengers were forced to spend the night at Birmingham Coach Station. There was also widespread disruption to train services. Shops throughout the Birmingham area had to close early on the last Saturday before Christmas and the severe cold spell was estimated to be costing the UK economy up to £1.2 billion a day with a total cost of £13 billion. Retailers were particularly badly hit with customer footfall across the country down twenty per cent compared to the same period the previous year and by as much as thirty per cent in the West Midlands and the South East. Not all shopkeepers were distraught, however, the online supermarket Ocado had seen a surge in demand for de-icer and the effects of the cold weather had also brought a 42% increase in sales of cough medicine. Tesco had also seen a spectacular rise in sales of de-icer and table salt which, with supplies of road grit and salt running out, was being pressed into service to clear domestic paths and driveways.

By 19 December a minimum temperature of -19.6°C was recorded at both Shawbury in Shropshire and Chesham in Buckinghamshire, and it was so cold in Banbury that the Oxford Canal was frozen solid. Heavy snow was also falling over large parts of Devon causing major travel disruption. Heathrow Airport was still badly affected with only twenty flights taking off out of a scheduled 1300. Heavy snow was also causing major problems in North East England.

Rail services to the continent were cancelled on 20 December, causing severe delays with queues snaking out of St Pancras station and stretching more than half a mile along Euston Road, past the British Library. At the same time domestic services were cancelled on the East Coast main line between London and Peterborough due to damage to the overhead power cables from the burden of ice.

The number of road accidents increased dramatically through drivers losing control of their cars on snow and ice.

It was so cold in mid-December 2010 that many canals froze solid.

A cyclist and solitary pedestrian brave bitter shopping conditions, which badly hit retailers in the run-up to Christmas.

As the bad weather spread further west on 21-22 December, there was heavy snow from the West Midlands to North Wales, and fifteen centimetres (six inches) of snow fell on parts of Dublin. Both Dublin Airport and City of Derry Airport were forced to close. Castlederg, in County Tyrone had recorded a new record low temperature for Northern Ireland of -18°C (-0.4°F) on the night of 19-20 December, but the record lasted just three days because on the morning of 23 December, the mercury at the same place dropped even further to -18.7°C (-1.66°F).

On Christmas Eve and Christmas Day, snow fell in many parts of the country with Scotland having its second consecutive White Christmas. It was also the coldest Christmas Day since 1830, with a Central England Temperature (CET) of -5.9 °C. It also proved to be a happy Christmas holiday for plumbers and heating engineers in Northern Ireland and Wales, as rising temperatures immediately after Christmas led to a bonanza of burst pipes and radiators. By 28 December thousands of homes and businesses were without water. Northern Ireland Water said that it was alternating supplies from reservoirs in order to help alleviate the crisis, with some properties without supplies since before Christmas.

The UK as a whole had endured the coldest December since 1890 and the second coldest December since records began in 1659. Places as far apart as Exeter, Belfast, Gravesend and Strathallan had all recorded their lowest ever temperatures, but once more, we were not alone, for northern Europe as a whole was suffering. Germany had its coldest December in forty years and the fourth coldest of the last 120 years, with an average temperature of -3.7°C, 4.5 °C below the long term mean temperature. There were also record snow falls for December in large parts of the country, though there was some consolation for the cold and disruption when the heavy snowfalls between 22 and 25 December gave the whole of Germany a white Christmas for the first time since 1981. However, snow and freezing rain caused horrendous conditions for those travelling home for the holiday, with road, rail and air travel all badly disrupted.

Although the Polish meteorologists most dire predictions of a "once in a thousand year winter" did not come true, the reality was bad enough. Eighteen Polish people died from exposure after temperatures fell as low as -26°C (-15°F). By December 18, Belgium had already recorded its snowiest ever winter with seventeen days of snowfall, and a few days later, on Christmas Eve, a church in Diepenbeek collapsed under the weight of snow on its roof.

The Swiss are not exactly unfamiliar with snow but even there, the severity of the weather this early in the winter took them by surprise. The heavy snow reported across the higher parts of the country on November 26 had spread to lowland Switzerland the next day, causing Geneva Airport to close. In France, a record low of -15.3°C (4°F) was recorded in Orleans on 30 November, the lowest sea level temperature ever recorded in France during the month of November. The frosts, ice and snow also caused a series of power cuts in the city.

Trondheim in Central Norway, also suffered its coldest November temperatures since records began, way back in 1788, and in the last week of the month the average daily temperatures were a whopping 12-14°C (22–25°F) below normal levels. Neighbouring Sweden and Denmark were also hit by severe blizzards, affecting road, rail and air travel. Sweden had its coldest and snowiest start to the winter in over a century and once more, low temperature records were broken with both Helsinki and Stockholm recording their coldest ever November nights, at -20°C (-4°F) and -17°C (1°F) respectively.

In the UK, by the end of December a widespread thaw had set in across the country, and the worst of the winter weather was already behind us. Although much milder than December, January 2011 was colder than average across the country, with a mean temperature of 3.1°C, but February was a very mild month with little frost and much of the country snow-free for the whole of February for the first time since 1998.

Things were very different in North America, where between 31 January and 2 February the "Groundhog Day Blizzard" - Groundhog Day, as immortalised by Bill Murray, falls on 2 February - was a winter storm of historic strength, with meteorologists stating that it would affect over 100 million people in the United States alone. The storm brought plunging temperatures and blizzard conditions all the way from New Mexico and northern Texas to New England and Eastern Canada. Chicago saw between one and two feet of snow and blizzard conditions, with winds of over sixty miles an hour lashing Lake Michigan into waves that buried shoreline structures and even a lighthouse under a thick carapace of ice. Blizzards also struck many other large cities, including Tulsa, Oklahoma City, Kansas City, St. Louis, Springfield, Des Moines, Milwaukee, Detroit, Indianapolis, Dayton, Cleveland, New York, and Boston. Other cities like Dallas and Houston, that were normally safe from extreme winter weather saw their first significant snow and ice in years.

An ice storm running ahead of the Groundhog Day storm also caused chaos from the Midwest to New England, with over an inch (2.5 centimetres) of ice clinging to every surface and turning roads and sidewalks into potential deathtraps. Temperatures plunged to 0°F (-18°C) as the storm passed and there were countless power cuts, airport closures and almost 20,000 flight cancellations, and chaos on many roads and railway services. Schools, government offices, and business and factories were closed, in some cases for several days. Even in states where the snow caused less problems, the storm had other tricks to play. There were tornados in Texas and Alabama, and "thundersnow" was reported in some places.

At least three dozen deaths were directly attributed to the effects of the storm, many of them people who had suffered strokes after the unaccustomed exertion of clearing deep snow from paths and driveways or who died in accidents on snow- or ice-bound roads. The most freakish death was that of a Chicago pedestrian who had been walking along the lakefront pathway in Chicago when the storm force winds blew him into Lake Michigan. His body was later recovered from the lake by Chicago Police.

The Groundhog Day storm was described as "the worst in fifty years" and its effects were so catastrophic that buildings were crushed under the weight of the ice and snow, and the total cost of the ice storm that preceded the great blizzard that followed it was alone predicted to be in excess of $1 billion, with the total bill set to reach $4 billion.

Now... aren't you glad you live in Britain?!

Possibly the coldest winter ever - the Thames during "The Great Frost of 1739". In the foreground a Frost Fair spreads across the ice and to the right figures can be seen inspecting the piers of the still incomplete Westminster Bridge. St Paul's dominates the London skyline in the background.

PART II

The Worst Winters in History

It's the old codger's lament: Things aren't what they used to be - 'We don't get summers/pork pies/films/footballers/music/cups of tea like we did when I was young'. In most cases, it's just the rose-tinted nostalgia of the old for the lost years of their youth, but in one case it is actually true: we really don't get winters like we used to any more.

Savage winters have been a recurring feature of our history as long as records have been kept. The Thames was frozen for nine weeks in 250 AD, and for thirteen weeks in 923 AD, when carts and wagons crossed the ice. In 1410, the river was frozen for fourteen weeks and winters were even more severe during the "Little Ice Age" between the middle of the sixteenth century and the middle of the nineteenth century. During the winter of 1536, Henry VIII was said to have travelled in a sleigh along the frozen River Thames all the way from the centre of London to Greenwich, and Elizabeth I took walks on the ice during the winter of 1564. The early years of the 1660s saw a succession of harsh winters. Skating was said to have been introduced into England during the winter of 1662/63; King Charles II watched the new sport on the frozen Thames. In the bitter winter of 1664-65, a severe frost lasting about two months included what was reputedly 'the coldest day ever in England'. The Thames froze from bank to bank above old London Bridge and a Frost Fair was held on ice 'so thick as to bear not only streets of booths in which they roasted meat, and divers shops of wares quite as in a town, but coaches, carts and horses.' Carriages took shortcuts across the frozen river rather than braving the traffic jams of vehicles - carts, carriages and wagons - and the droves of animals and hordes of pedestrians that, then as now, reduced traffic over the bridge to a crawl. There was even a bonfire on the ice, not perhaps the wisest place to light one, but it passed off without incident.

The winter of 1683-84 may have been the coldest ever. The 'Great Frost' began in mid-December 1683 and by early January the Thames was frozen all the way to London Bridge. The diarist John Evelyn called the winter 'intolerably severe'. The frost, claimed to be the longest on record, kept the Thames frozen for two months, with as much as eleven inches of solid ice covering the surface. Evelyn rode in a coach along the frozen river all the way from London Bridge to Lambeth, 'Coaches plied from Westminster to the Temple, and from several other stairs too and fro, as in the streets, sleds, sliding with skates, bull-baiting, horse and coach races, puppet plays and interludes, cooks, tippling and other lewd places, so that it seemed to be a bacchanalian triumph, or carnival on the water.' It was so cold that by January the Company of Watermen was distributing £200 to 'poor watermen' deprived by the ice of their normal source of income - the river.

Near Manchester, the ground froze to a depth of twenty-seven inches, and in Somerset, to an incredible depth of four feet. RD Blackmore, in *Lorna Doone*, described the winter on Exmoor. "An ancient shepherd had dropped in, and taken supper with us, and foretold a heavy fall [of snow] and great disaster to livestock. He said that he had known a frost beginning, just as this had done, with a black east wind, after days of raw cold fog, and then on the third night of the frost at this very time of year (to wit the 15th of December) such a snow set in as killed half of the sheep, and many even of the red deer and the forest ponies... Two of his toes had been lost by frost-nip, while he dug out his sheep...

"All the birds were set in one direction, steadily journeying westward, not with any heat

A VIEW OF FROST FAIR, ON THE THAMES, February 1814. (8)

The Year 1814 will be long remembered for the severe frosts and heavy falls of snow with which it commenced, and by which the rivers were rendered innavigable, and the public roads for several days impassable. At the beginning of February the river was completely blocked up with ice, between London and Blackfriars Bridges, where a fair was kept, 3 or 4 days, with booths, swings, skittles, presses printing tickets in commemoration, &c. &c.
Published by T. Batchelar, 115, Long Alley, Moorfields.

The last ever great frost fair held on the Thames in 1814. A fire is blazing in the tent in the right foreground, to the left are street vendors and a printing press set up on the ice. Ships are frozen into the river but the ice is thin enough for people to be depicted falling through it. In the background is Blackfriars Bridge.

of speed, neither flying far at once; but all (as if on business bound) partly running, partly flying, partly fluttering along; silently, and without a voice, neither pricking head nor tail. This movement of the birds went on, even for a week or more; every kind of thrushes passed us, every kind of wild fowl, even plovers went away, and crows and snipes and woodcocks. And before half the frost was over, all we had in the snowy ditches were hares so tame that we could pat them; partridges that came to hand, with a dry noise in their crops; heath-poults, making cups of snow; and a few poor hopping redwings, flapping in and out of the hedge, having lost the power to fly. And all the time, their great black eyes, set with gold around them, seemed to look at any man for mercy and for comfort...

"Of the sheep upon the mountain, and the sheep upon the western farm, and the cattle on the upper burrows, scarcely one in ten was saved... The great snow never ceased a moment for three days and nights, and then when all the earth was filled, and topmost hedges were unseen, and the trees broke down with weight (wherever the wind had not lightened them), a brilliant sun broke forth and showed the loss of all our customs. All our house was quite snowed up, except where we had purged a way by dint of constant shovellings, the kitchen was as dark and darker than the cider-cellar, and long lines of furrowed scollops ran even up to the chimney stacks. Several windows fell right inwards, through the weight of the snow against them; and the few that stood bulged in and bent like an old bruised lanthorn [lantern]. We were obliged to cook by candlelight; we were forced to read by candlelight; as for baking, we could not do it, because the oven was too chill.

"That night such a frost ensued as we had never dreamed of, neither read in ancient books, or histories of [the Arctic voyages of] Frobisher. The kettle by the fire froze, and the crock upon the hearth-cheeks; many men were killed, and cattle rigid in their head-ropes. Then I heard that fearful sound, which never I heard before, neither since have heard (except during that same winter), the sharp yet solemn sound of trees, burst open by the frost-blow. Our great walnut lost three branches, and has been dying ever since... and the ancient oak at the cross was rent, and many score of ash-trees... It mattered not what way the wind was. Often and often the vanes went around, and we hoped for change of weather: the only change was that it seemed (if possible) to grow colder... But why should I tell all this? The people who have not seen it (as I have) will only make faces and disbelieve, till such another frost comes; which perhaps may never be."

The winter of 1694-95 saw five weeks of 'continual snows', and ended only around mid-April, by which time Britain had endured almost six months of winter, while the unfortunate inhabitants of Iceland had seen the Arctic sea ice extend far south of its usual limit, to encircle the entire Icelandic coast. Six winters in that decade were very severe and the cumulative effect of the run of poor harvests saw many peasant farmers starve to death.

In 1715-16 the Thames was frozen for two months, and a frost fair took place on the ice. On 25 January the ice was 'lifted by some fourteen feet by a flood tide' but it was so thick that it did not break. 1739-40 saw one of the worst - and certainly one of the coldest - winters since records began. Winter came unusually early - on 8 October - and at one point the Thames remained frozen for eight weeks. A violent easterly gale on 29-30 December drove large blocks of drifting ice before it and caused substantial damage to the piers of London Bridge and shipping on the Thames. Many ships were driven ashore and dashed to pieces. 16 January 1740 was described as 'the coldest day in the memory of man', Spring was also cold and miserable and the following October was the coldest on record, with ice already forming on rivers. After two successive years of terrible winters and failed harvests, 1741 was known in Ireland as bliadhain an áir - the year of the slaughter - with an estimated 300,000 dead of starvation, ten percent of the total population. A pamphlet, "The Groans of Ireland", described 'Want and misery in every face... the roads spread with dead and dying bodies; mankind the colour of the docks and nettles which they fed on; two or three, sometimes more, in a cart going to the grave for want of bearers to carry them, and many buried only in the fields and ditches where they perished.'

In 1784-86, two successive severe winters followed the repeated eruptions of the Icelandic volcano Laki, in 1783 and 1784. In Iceland itself, the winter of 1783-84 was known as "The Famine Winter" in which a quarter of the population died. Reports from all over Europe spoke of 'a blue haze' or 'dry-fog' in the atmosphere and damage to plants and crops, and there were numerous complaints of respiratory problems. The effect on the British weather was equally pronounced. The Thames froze completely in both winters, there were near-continuous frosts, and lying snow for four months. Sleet was recorded near the coast of the Moray Firth in August 1784 and heavy snow fell in the South on 7 October. The last substantial snowfall of the winter came six months later on 4 April.

In January 1789, during another Frost Fair on the Thames, melting ice dragged a ship anchored to a riverside public house, pulling the building down and crushing five people to death. 1794-95 was another exceptionally severe winter, beginning on Christmas Eve and lasting until late March. It included the coldest January since weather recording by instruments began in 1659. The Severn and The Thames froze, and Frost Fairs were held.

In 1813-1814, thick fog and sharp frosts on 27 December heralded the start of a bitterly cold winter. The fog was so dense that the Birmingham mail coach took seven hours to travel the sixteen miles from Central London to Uxbridge in Middlesex. On 30 and 31 December, traffic was almost at a standstill in London and coachmen had to dismount and lead their horses through the streets. Bitter northerly winds cleared the fog in early January, but brought heavy snowfall and frosts so severe that ice floating down the Thames during a brief thaw between 5 and 7 February caused severe damage to shipping. The tidal stretch of the Thames froze and the last great Frost Fair was held on the river. An elephant was led across the river below Blackfriars Bridge, and a printer named Davis published a book entitled *Frostiana; Or a History of the River Thames in a Frozen State*. The narrow arches and thick stone piers of the old London Bridge had greatly restricted the river flow, making it far more likely to freeze. The increased flow after the construction of the new London Bridge prevented ice from forming to anything like the same extent and no more great Frost Fairs were ever held.

The following year, the eruption of Tambora in the East Indies on 10 April 1815 killed 90,000 people and blasted debris and millions of tons of sulphur dioxide into the stratosphere. While the fine particles suspended in the air produced some spectacular sunsets worldwide for over a year afterwards, the eruption also disrupted global weather patterns and made Britain unusually cold and wet. The following year, 1816, was known as "the year of no summer" and was followed by a bleak and very prolonged winter. There was ice on the Thames on 2 September of that year and on 20 October 'a great hurricane and snowstorm' struck northern Scotland. 'The stooks of corn were yet out in the fields, and the snow had to be cast to get at them; when dug out they were a frozen lump, and could not be thawed for the cattle.' There were still snow drifts on Helvellyn in the Lake District on 30 July of the

A caricature of Patrick Murphy, "the Dick-tater, alias the weather-cock of the walk", the celebrated prophet of "Murphy's Winter" of 1837-38. Master of all weathers, a weather vane sticks out of the top of his potato head, he has a globe for a body, and holds bellows and a telescope under his right arm, and an umbrella and a watering can under his left. His right foot is bare, and his left foot is in a snow shoe.

MURPHY THE DICK-TATER,
ALIAS THE WEATHER COCK OF THE WALK.
A Statue to be erected near the Change.

following year. The harvest across Europe was delayed and in Ireland and western parts of Britain there was a total crop failure, leading to widespread starvation.

1837-38, "Murphy's Winter", was so named in honour of Patrick Murphy, who won fame and fortune from the sale of an almanac in which he predicted the severe frost of January 1838. 20 January saw temperatures as low as -16°C in London, the coldest recorded in the capital throughout the 19th century, and even at midday the temperature at Greenwich had risen no higher than -11°C. Spring planting was delayed, and frosts in August, continuing through September and October wrecked the harvest and caused frost-damage to root crops leading to severe hardship and even starvation for tenant farmers.

In 1875-76, significant snowfall was recorded in November, December, January, February, March, April and May, making it one of the most prolonged winters ever. In the first week of December blizzards left one to two feet of level snow over the South-East and as late as April, snowstorms dumped almost two feet of snow on the Midlands.

ICE IN THE THAMES AT LONDON BRIDGE.

An 1870s view of the frozen River Thames, looking north from just below London Bridge.

In December 1894 'the worst storm of the century' struck Britain, toppling thousands of trees and damaging roofs and church spires throughout the country. The calm that followed heralded the start of 'the twelve week frost' beginning on 30 December. In mid-February the whole of the Thames was said to be blocked by ice-floes six or seven feet thick. An ox was roasted on the river at Kingston and coaches crossed on the ice at Oxford. Thousands skated on the frozen Serpentine in London and on Windermere in the Lake District, which was frozen solid for six weeks. Thousands of people arrived in the Lake District by train, bands played in Bowness Bay and crowds of over two thousand people skated on the ice, rode bicycles fitted with spiked tyres, sailed 'ice-yachts', and ate and drank at stalls erected on the frozen lake.

In the twentieth century, 1916-17 was the year in which thousands of soldiers already enduring the miseries of trench warfare and the aftermath of the disastrous Battle of the Somme on the Western Front, had to suffer 'the worst winter in twenty years' as well. Soldiers 'lying at each listening post were freezing stiff, and would take half an hour's buffeting and rubbing on return to avoid becoming casualties.' Many men on both sides died

The frozen River Thames in 1895.

A train on the Highland Railway in Scotland, near Altnabreac in 1895, where the drifts were forty to fifty feet deep. Drivers of steam engines fitted with snowploughs - first used in the 1850s - often tried to ram their way through drifts but some were derailed in the process.

A man standing in a rowing boat frozen into the river, surveys the towering ice-floes on the Thames in 1895.

of frostbite and hypothermia, and in conditions where even survival was a daily battle, both sides restricted their aggressive actions to sporadic sniping, artillery duels and small raids on the enemy trenches. An army chaplain, David Railton, described the conditions in a letter to his wife. 'Today there was an inspection. The men were not kept there long. Still two of them fainted from cold.... Even the Sacred Wine in the Chalice froze on Sunday. Our men are very, very brave. Some of them could not bear their boots on this last time up the line. They put sandbags around their feet... We have thirty degrees of frost out here.'

A soldier in the reserve areas 'had to light a fire of paper in boots frozen hard before they

A boy walking his dog through the deep snow covering the beach at Whitby in the winter of 1904-5. The boy is up to his thighs and the dog is almost buried.

were pliable enough to put on. One learnt the lesson that it was necessary to sleep with one's boots in bed with one and, strange to believe, make them part of one's pillow.' Another soldier reported 'suffering badly from frost-bitten feet. My hands had swollen to twice their normal size and frequently my arms were completely numbed up to the elbows. For nearly a month I had not had my boots off and most of my companions were in the same miserable state as myself, owing to the intense cold... Putting the backs of my swollen hands to the barrel of my rifle, I could feel nothing, and I could only lift it up by holding it between my elbows. God help us if we had been called upon to defend ourselves. Fifty yards away [the enemy] were, no doubt, thinking the same thing. Frostbite was a terrible enemy, how terrible only those who lived in the trenches for weeks on end knew. Men were actually being frozen to death and others were fighting against sleep and cold until they could fight no longer.'

As that soldier had surmised, the German soldiers were in the same miserable state. As one, Paul Hub, remarked, 'Through all those wet, snowy, cold days, we were lying, wet through and with chattering teeth in the mud and filth of holes that we had dug ourselves in the ground.' The one benefit of the weather came when lice-ridden soldiers put their shirts out in the frost to freeze the lice to death and then warmed their shirts by sitting on them before putting them back on. Unfortunately, like all the other remedies against lice, it offered no more than temporary relief before the itching, scratching plague returned.

In 1932-33, snow fell in Scotland in October and from 23 to 26 February there was a "Great Blizzard" with gales and prolonged snowstorms, prompting the Met Office to issue its first ever warning about disruption to traffic. Whipsnade recorded 24 inches of level snow, Buxton 28 inches and Harrogate and Huddersfield 30 inches, and there were drifts of fifteen to twenty feet on the hills.

The winter of 1939-40, the first of the Second World War, was one of the longest and snowiest of the century. January 1940 saw savage cold, heavy snow and deep drifting right

Britain's highest pub, The Tan Hill Inn, half-buried by drifts.

A tidal stretch of the River Ouse frozen solid in the winter of 1939-40. The harshness of the winter compounded the misery of wartime Britain.

Ships frozen into the river while waiting to load at Scott's Mill, Selby in 1940.

across the country - Sheffield had a four-foot snowfall towards the end of the month. The West Highland railway line in Scotland was blocked and a train was also snowbound a few miles south of Preston for thirty-six hours. On 27 January rain fell on frozen ground over a swathe of land stretching from North Wales across the Midlands to the South-West and central-southern England. The ice remained intact for a week, lasting until 3 February, causing massive transport disruption and hundreds of injuries to people slipping and falling.

British families endured the privations of war far into peacetime, with rationing in force on some products until 1954, almost a decade after the end of the war, and in 1947 a winter occurred that piled further miseries upon them - perhaps the most harsh winter ever experienced.

29,325 supporters enduring a blizzard at the F.A. Cup fifth-round tie between Halifax and Luton in 1933

PART III

The Snowiest Winter – 1947

There have been colder winters than 1947 - though not many - but no winter since records began has ever been as snowy. It began gently enough. There had been snowfalls before Christmas and again in early January 1947, but both had melted within days and by the middle of that month, the temperature was unseasonably warm. At Leeming in North Yorkshire it remained in double figures throughout the night of 15-16 January, and the next day, it rose to a balmy 14°C right across the country, from Norfolk in the East to Herefordshire and Flintshire in the West, prompting optimists to begin looking forward to spring. It was to be a long time coming.

The weather turned colder again on 20 January, with a sharp frost that night and the next. On the 22nd, clouds the colour of pewter began to mass, building from the south-west, and it started to snow in mid-afternoon. A few flurries of sleet and wet snow fell at first, melting almost as soon as they touched the ground, but the snow continued and intensified throughout the evening and night, driven before a fierce wind. The heaviest falls were over the South and South-West of England, where the blizzard was the worst recorded since 1891; many villages in Devon were cut off. Even the Isles of Scilly had a few centimetres of snow, an almost unheard of occurrence.

As the snow began to fall, the government was in crisis over plummeting stocks of coal and food. The country was still largely dependent on the rail network for the movement of people and supplies. There were no motorways, relatively few lorries and no large-scale programme of salting and gritting the roads in bad weather. There were few convenience foods, or imported foodstuffs, very few fridges and even if food had been plentiful, most families had no money to spare for anything but necessities. A Government spokesman, Lord Henderson, chose this moment to announce 'profoundly gloomy forecasts of Britain's food position'. The fresh meat ration was cut from one shilling and twopence (six pence) to a shilling (five pence) of which the portion that had to be taken as 'corned meat' - usually Argentinean corned beef - increased from 2d to 4d. There was 'no hope' of restoring the three ounce ration of bacon and 'probably difficulty in maintaining the two ounce ration' and a reduction in the bread ration 'may be inescapable'. The one feeble consolation he could offer was on the supply of eggs, with 'a good chance that they will not be fewer than last year'.

A lorry fitted with a snowplough struggling to clear snow from a moorland road. The driver's workmates stand ready to dig him out if he gets stuck.

As Lord Cherwell - Winston Churchill's Personal Assistant during the War - pointed out in the angry debate that followed the announcement, 'We are faced with the stark fact that in the first year of peace we had less than in the last year of war,' and Lord Wootton complained of 'a harassing unhappiness to the housewives of the nation'. The morale of their menfolk would not have been improved by the news that a fifty per cent cut in their coal allocation was forcing brewers to announce a halving of beer production 'for at least six weeks'. Coal was in such short supply that at least one gas works closed because of a lack of its raw material and many other industries were on short-time working, and the first heavy snows over the weekend of 24 to 25 January produced power-cuts of ten, fifteen and then twenty per cent throughout the country, lasting from twenty minutes to two hours.

The onset of the winter storms could only exacerbate the problems. The temperature barely rose above freezing that day or the next, and there were further heavy falls of snow spreading northwards over the whole of England and Wales. The level snow was up to a foot deep and drifts more than fifteen feet deep blocked countless roads and railways from Cornwall to Kent and northwards as far as the Scottish border. A line of abandoned lorries and cars on Wrotham Hill in Kent stretched for two miles. Salt and grit were rarely used in those days and if roads were cleared at all, the snowploughs left behind a two inch layer of hard-packed snow. Motorists either left their cars in their garages and walked, or fitted tyre-chains. So regular and predictable was the annual post-Christmas cold snap, that many motorists kept a set of spare wheels with old, bald tyres permanently fitted with chains. When the winter snows came, they swapped wheels and kept the chains in place until the spring thaw. In every area, but especially in the industrial North and Midlands, the pristine snow soon turned darker and greyer as coal smuts and fine ash from house- and mill-chimneys drifted down. By the time the snow finally melted it was often covered with a grey-black crust.

The hard frosts covered ponds and lakes with ice, an enticing sight for children. During the weekend of 25 and 26 January, four children died as a result of 'venturing onto frozen ponds' - the first lives to be claimed by the winter weather. Two boys, aged nine and fourteen, were drowned near Maidenhead after their sledge, improvised from the chassis of an old pram, broke through the ice of a frozen pond, and six year-old Raymond Bailey and his eight year-old sister, Sheila, both drowned when the ice broke while they were sliding on a frozen pond near Newport in Shropshire.

On Sunday 26 January gales were pounding 'the East Coast and the shores of the Channel', and conditions were so bad at London Airport [Heathrow] that though BOAC services to Sydney and New York left London, 'two for Cairo' were cancelled and only one inbound flight was able to land all day. Rail and road transport was badly affected by snow and ice and in Leeds bus and tram services were also hit by the number of drivers and conductors - 260 - off work with colds and flu. By the morning of 27 January, roads in Devon were buried under ten-foot drifts, and 100 miles of Kent roads were also blocked. The Rochester to Maidstone road was covered by seven foot drifts and the Whitstable to Canterbury road also 'impassable'. The Isle of Sheppey was cut off and sledges were being used for milk deliveries in Hampstead and Southend. Two fire engines from Clacton and Colchester, called to a fire at Walton-on-the-Naze, were stopped by snowdrifts and the fire had to be left to burn itself out.

The following day, 28 January, snow fell continuously in Eastbourne for ten hours. In

Essex, the road from Clacton to Harwich was blocked by drifts, the Piccadilly and Central Lines on the London Underground suffered delays and cancellations because of snow and a funeral at Sheerness was cancelled because it was impossible to reach the crematorium. The temperature dropped to record levels. It fell to -20.6°C at Writtle in Essex that night and the following night it was -21.3°C at Elmstone in Kent and -23°C at Luton - among the coldest nights ever recorded. In London, an afternoon snowstorm was followed by the coldest night for 66 years. 'Midnight listeners noted sympathetically a lapse on the part of Big Ben under the influence of the frost. Only a few fragmentary notes of the well-known chimes were sounded and the clock struck one. After that there was silence.' Roads throughout the North were reported to be 'icebound', frost formed on internal walls, ice covered the inside of bedroom windows, and in Bradford, Yorkshire, one old woman later recalled that her false teeth had frozen in the glass she kept next to the bed.

The misery was compounded by shortages of domestic fuel, threats of all-day power-cuts and reduced gas supplies. On 29 January Cardiff was plunged into darkness for almost three hours and there was a record twenty-five per cent cut in electricity supplies throughout South-East England. There were even more dire warnings of day-long cuts to come and the Gas, Light and Coke Company warned users to keep gas appliances 'under observation as the gas might go out without the knowledge of the users'. In London's Hyde Park, the gates were closed at sunset and the gas lighting left unlit, as was the case in many other parts of the capital. In all, 1,400 miles of streets throughout London were left in darkness, other than 'the thousands of hurricane lamps placed on bollards and street refuges'.

There was more heavy snow in the South and South-West; once again 'the worst blizzards since 1891'. There were twelve foot drifts on Dartmoor, leaving many cars stranded, and Princetown and Dartmoor Prison cut off. There were ten foot drifts on Exmoor, while Falmouth had a foot of snow, its heaviest snowfall in living memory. London express trains suffered long delays while gangs worked to clear blocked cuttings between Plymouth and Newton Abbot, and the express from Penzance took twenty hours to reach Crewe. Salcombe was completely cut off and food had to be brought in by boat from Kingsbridge, while in turn, the Salcombe lifeboat was then called out to deliver bread to Hope Cove.

Even the Scilly Isles had 'a heavy snowfall, an experience not remembered for fifty years', followed by four degrees of frost. Further east, the Thames froze at Windsor, the Medway was icebound at Tonbridge and for eight miles downstream, and the sea froze in Folkestone harbour. Schools in Oxford, Hove and Dover closed because of frozen pipes, and Bristol ambulance crews received twenty calls to attend people who had collapsed in the snow-covered streets from the cold. The RSPCA urged people to bring their cats and dogs in at night and to put out 'table scraps' for the wild birds. Primroses and snowdrops already in bloom in West Wales 'fought bravely for life in nine degrees of frost'. To add insult to injury, Reuters reported that Iceland was enjoying 'warm, spring-like weather. Flowers are blooming even on the North Coast, a few miles from the Arctic Circle.'

The Icelandic winter appeared to have moved south and in the North of England, Yorkshire had its heaviest snowfall of the winter so far. A blizzard beginning at dusk raged all night and roads only reopened at the weekend when 'one vehicle-width tracks were cut through the snow' were completely filled in and blocked again. Phone lines came down, cutting off many isolated areas from the outside world. Thousands of hill sheep were lost, buried under the drifts.

Non-mechanical horsepower staged something of a comeback in the winter of 1947.

Percy Lambert, a postman at Thixendale, wearing 'gumboots, a thick overcoat and a muffler over his head', walked his 21-mile round, skirting drifts six feet deep. It took him from 7.30 am to six in the evening, but he was out again first thing the next morning; as the postmistress said, 'His motto is: the post goes through'. Over the course of the week, he covered over 120 miles on foot through the thick snow. One of his customers, Fred Dawson, of Riggs Farm, near Thixendale, had seen 'not a soul' for a week and was further isolated as 'his wireless battery is discharged. Shortage of water is his worst trouble. There is no road through to the only supply of drinking water - a roadside tap two miles from the farm.' His stock depended on a frozen dew-pond from which water had to be 'ladled through a hole in the ice.'

Throughout Britain, soaring demand for fuel, reduced output from the collieries, problems with distribution because of the weather and shortages of locomotives and rolling stock, were combining to make an already bad situation even worse. Iron, steel and engineering works were forced to reduce production, Lancashire cotton mills and Yorkshire wool mills went on to short-time working or closed down altogether, the Abbey Paper Mills in Holywell, North Wales, shut down, and in Leeds 5,000 workers were sent home because of power-cuts.

An AA Box near Merthyr Tydfil almost buried by snow drifts.

Shoe factories in Northampton were 'at a standstill' and workers at the Austin Motor Company's Longbridge factory in Birmingham were told that fuel shortages meant that until further notice, they would be restricted to working 'one day in ten or one five day week in ten weeks'. The government issued warnings that nationwide power-cuts would be imposed from seven in the morning to seven at night if the situation did not improve. To reinforce the warnings, on 30 January there were 'the heaviest cuts in gas and electricity supplies yet experienced' - twenty-five per cent. Standpipes were installed in the streets because the pipes in so many houses were completely frozen and even where water was flowing, waterworks in Cambridge and other towns and cities warned that there would be cuts in supply because of the scale of leaks from broken pipes.

On top of rationing and other food shortages, milk was now in short supply with mounting stocks of uncollected milk on the farms. Some farmers struggled across the fields, hauling churns on sledges but even then, dairy lorries often could not get through to collect them and on many farms milk hadn't been picked up for four days. In the midst of this and other food shortages, there was outrage at the owners of a Bournemouth hotel prosecuted for 'receiving 9,000 eggs during a period when it was entitled to only 1,980 - a complete black market in eggs'. The eggs had been pickled and 'stored in a room entered by a trapdoor'. Future egg-supplies throughout Britain were threatened by the death of thousands of chicks in incubators after cuts in the electricity supply. On 31 January there were even worse reductions with twenty-five per cent cuts in electricity and even more savage cuts in gas supplies - fifty per cent in North Middlesex.

Worse was to come as Britain endured the coldest February since records began in 1659. The month began with a brief flicker of a thaw - on the first day of February the temperature reached 6°C at Penzance and on the Air Ministry roof in London it rose above freezing for the first time in eight days, but by six that evening it was back below zero. The next day a twelve hour blizzard hit the North - once more 'the worst of the winter'. Six-foot drifts cut off Edale in Derbyshire and every trans-Pennine route was blocked, apart from the road over Blackstone Edge, kept open by 'the constant use of snowploughs'. The driver and conductor of a bus from Settle to Horton-in-Ribblesdale had to dig themselves out of drifts 'three times with garden spades', and the power lines to Hemsworth were brought down during evensong at the village church. 'Candles were lighted and after tapers were distributed to the congregation, the hymn "All Things Bright and Beautiful" was sung.'

The blizzards and gales paralysed shipping traffic too. In the North-East, Seaham harbour was closed because of gales and high seas, and on the opposite coast, passengers on the Isle of Man packet steamer *Mona's Queen*, who had already been waiting at Liverpool for two days, 'last night settled down to another weary wait at the landing stages as they had been told through loudspeakers that the earliest departure would be at four o'clock this morning, and then only if the weather cleared.'

Meanwhile, HMS Vanguard, bearing the King and Queen and Princesses Elizabeth and Margaret away from frozen Britain for a six-week state visit to South Africa, was battered by the same storm in the Bay of Biscay. 'Heavy seas smashed gratings on HMS Vanguard's deck and broke adrift a piano in the ship's schoolroom', and the Royal Family spent most of the day quietly in their quarters.

The next morning, the 250 ton trawler *Elsie Cam* sank at the mouth of Grimsby harbour after it had 'battled for several hours with one of the worst blizzards the Lincolnshire Coast

Sledgers trudge up a hill on the outskirts of Glasgow while a football match goes ahead despite the hard-frozen pitch.

had known.' Police officers patrolling the sea-front 'had difficulty in staying upright against what one described as "a hurricane".' Captain Almond, the skipper of the trawler, sent a last radio message, 'Just about had it. Don't think you can do anything for us. Give my love to wife and kiddies. Can't last. Goodbye. Gone.' In fact, although the trawler sank, he and his nine-man crew were all rescued from the freezing sea.

By the next day, 3 February, continuing snow had left Buxton in Derbyshire cut off by road and rail, power lines had been brought down in County Durham, 'plunging a large area around Tow Law into darkness' and traffic was 'at a standstill' in many parts of the country. The Leeds-Liverpool Canal was frozen solid at Skipton, holding up barges laden with coal. Ice on the transmitter at Moorside Edge forced BBC programmes off the air in the North, 'believed to be the first time in this country that a "hold-up" has been caused in such a way.' At Castle Hill near Huddersfield, three double-decker buses were 'marooned' in snow drifts, along with 'another bus, equipped with a snowplough, which had gone to their rescue and then got stuck itself.' Mr RC Chadwick, a postman in the Kirkburton district, 'sank up to his chin in a snowdrift and had to burrow his way out with his hands.' During the FA Cup replay at Leicester City that night, two Brentford footballers begged the referee to abandon the game because of the blizzard that was raging, but he refused, perhaps feeling that the 4-1 scoreline in Leicester's favour might have had something to do with their pleas. Late that night 'with the aid of lights from snowploughs', teams of men dug through drifts on Dartmoor from Princetown to Yelverton, about eight miles away, to enable an ambulance to take two women in need of medical treatment to hospital.

The snow was falling as heavy rain in East Anglia and there were floods in Chelmsford, Ipswich and Felixstowe, but elsewhere in Britain there was only an endless expanse of white. The next day, 4 February, the snow was even heavier - 'the worst day's blizzard ever remembered', continuing non-stop for over twenty-four hours. Forty villages in Leicestershire were cut off, the Vale of Belvoir was blocked by seven foot drifts, there were ten foot drifts at Cromer in Norfolk, and on high ground in the North the drifts reached twenty feet and more. The AA reported that 'all roads were impassable in Derbyshire' and that 'snowdrifts several feet deep' were making road travel 'virtually impossible' throughout the North Midlands and the North. 600 vehicles were caught between Grantham and Stamford, and the Settle-Carlisle railway line was blocked virtually all the way through the Pennines; 'for miles the lines were indiscernible'. Four engines of the LMS railway were derailed at Low Moor, Bradford, and the roofs of Grantham and Wakefield stations collapsed under the weight of snow. At Grantham a seventy-five yard stretch of the roof caved in, completely blocking the up and down main lines only seconds after an LNER express train had passed through. A 300-foot section of the roof of the Avro factory at Yeadon in Yorkshire also collapsed under the weight of snow, fortunately a few minutes before the men arrived for work.

The misery was not confined to Britain; the whole of the Northern hemisphere seemed to be gripped by ice and snow, with a temperature of -78.7° Fahrenheit - 110 degrees of frost - at Snag airport in the Yukon, 'the coldest weather ever recorded on the North American continent'. It was reported from Berlin that fifty-three Germans had been found frozen to death on a refugee train from Poland when it arrived at Dresden.

In Britain, there were tales of lesser, but still considerable hardship from every quarter. A party of seventy-eight people, many of them elderly, returning by charabanc to Pickering in

Undertakers were forced to turn to horsepower as blocked roads prevented motor hearses from getting through.

North Yorkshire after a trip to see the pantomime in Whitby were trapped overnight on the moors by snowdrifts. Some of the passengers 'fainted from the cold during the night'. A motorist who came across them 'tramped for four hours over the snow to Market Weighton, four miles away', to alert rescuers. The next morning the trapped passengers were led on foot to the nearest village, Lockton, where they were housed by villagers until the storm abated.

Another busload of sixty pantomime-goers, returning to Littondale from Bradford, struggled through the snow to the Devonshire Arms at Bolton Abbey, 'where they were accommodated in the hotel ballroom'. Three members of the party, all dairy farmers 'anxious to get home to their farms in time for milking,' then set off at two-thirty in the morning to make a seventeen mile trudge through blinding snow and deep drifts. They did not reach their farms until after lunchtime that day. Thirty-five other members of their party were still at Bolton Abbey three days later. The crew of an ambulance from the Keighley District Victoria Hospital used a sledge to carry a seventy-five year-old woman a mile and a half over the snow to their ambulance, and two doctors fought their way through nine miles of drifts in Wensleydale to rescue a nine year-old girl suffering from appendicitis. Yet, for one six year-old Leeds girl, the snow was a life-saver. The girl had been 'dancing too near the fireplace' when her 'loose frock' caught fire. She ran out of her house with her clothing ablaze and a neighbour, a sixty-nine year-old widow, rolled the little girl in the snow to put out the flames. One man already beyond any but divine help, was carried to his funeral in Holmfirth by 'a special sleigh' constructed by the undertaker, 'as it was impossible to use a hearse' because of the snow.

There was great alarm over the fate of a couple from Kensington in London. Estate agent Richard Grisham and his wife Joy had disappeared while on holiday in the North York Moors. Despite the snow, they left their hotel at Goathland to walk to Egton Bridge and had not been seen since. They were still missing three days later, when 'grave fears' were being expressed about their safety. Police fought their way through snowdrifts of twenty feet to reach all but three outlying farms; 'The one hope we have,' a police spokesman said, 'is that Mr and Mrs Grisham reached one of these.' Meanwhile those able to obtain a newspaper were informed that 'the King and Queen and the two princesses were out on the open deck yesterday, as HMS Vanguard entered warm sunshine and calmer seas off Morocco.'

Councils were now using bulldozers and mechanical diggers to try to clear snow from blocked roads and contractors normally working on opencast coal mines were put to work with their diggers and grablines. German and Italian prisoners of war and members of the Polish Resettlement Corps were also issued with shovels and put to work - 'as soon as Polish troops at Blackshaw Moor camp between Leek and Buxton have dug themselves out, 2,000 will go to Buxton to help in snow clearance'. However, the weather continued to frustrate efforts to get Britain moving again.

Virtually every commodity, particularly coal and foodstuffs, was in desperately short supply. The movement of coal by land and sea was badly hit by the blizzards and gales, and gas and electricity supplies were constantly threatened by the shortages of fuel. Thirty-seven vessels, fully loaded with coal, were trapped by the gales in North-East ports and a further thirty, empty, were immobilised in London. It would have required 150-200 coal trains to move the fuel by land, but there were no spare trains available and in any case, most lines were blocked by snow.

Virtually every Pennine town and village was running out of bread and food, and with Buxton still cut off and desperately short of supplies, 'lorries laden with fresh meat' and other supplies were waiting at New Mills to 'rush in food' as soon as roads could be opened. Even in the lowlands, the situation was often desperate. A woman in Warrington, who had no fuel and was also running out of food, remembers pushing a pram four miles through the snow to collect a sack of coal and a loaf of bread. Dairies in many places were now delivering milk only to those with "priority permits" - nursing mothers, hospitals and schools - and a spokesman for the Craven Dairies in North Yorkshire doubted if there was even enough for them. There was a glut of uncollected milk on farms and 'hand-turned churns were being used for the first time in years' to turn some of the milk into butter before it went sour.

By 6 February, 60,000 workers were idle in Birmingham alone and the government was forced to impose 'drastic restrictions on railway and sea-borne traffic to relieve the critical coal supply position caused by blizzards on land and gales at sea, as the tally of industrial concerns forced by coal shortages to close down continues to grow.' The Ford Motor Company at Dagenham was the latest to shut down, 8,000 workers at Cadburys in Bourneville were sent home for ten days and 2,000 workers at the Goodyear tyre factory were also laid off 'for an indefinite period'. Two Co-operative depots in Sheffield, supplying sixty per cent of the city's

A steam train embedded in a huge drift. Aisgill, 1947.

population with milk, had to send their workers home because they had no milk at all.

A ban was imposed on the export of coal, railway companies were ordered to 'curtail general traffic to expedite the movement of coal at all costs,' and power stations were given 'prior call' on coal stocks, though 'domestic supplies would not be touched, except as a last resort.' Efforts to improve coal production and distribution were hampered by a series of problems. Many families reliant on open fires as their only source of heating had already used up their coal and could obtain no fresh supplies as coal merchants were snowed in their yards. Eight pits in Nottinghamshire and Derbyshire and two in Northumberland had to close because of 'a lack of coal wagons', colliery sidings in the North-East were blocked by snow and the coal docks at Barry and Cardiff were paralysed by the 'freezing up of loading devices'. One industrialist, GB Warman of Shenstone Air Developments in Lichfield, shut his factory and issued an appeal to all his workers to 'volunteer to go down the coal mines in this country's hour of need.' The response was 'so gratifying and, he admits, amazing, that he has passed on the idea to Mr Lord, General Manager of the Austin Motor Company at Longbridge, where 15,000 workers are now idle.' 'The relief of coal-starved London' began

On some trans-Pennine roads, vehicles were stranded for weeks.

on 7 February with the arrival of seven colliers off Tilbury, carrying 18,000 tons of coal.' Meanwhile 'a concentrated attack' by bulldozers backed by an army of hundreds of men with shovels, opened several main roads through the Pennines.

The search for the Grishams, the Kensington couple missing somewhere on the Yorkshire Wolds, was called off the same day after a telegram handed in at Jermyn Street Post Office in London was received in North Yorkshire. Without bothering to inform anyone, the Grishams, it seemed, had simply gone home, leaving their luggage to be collected at some later point. A police spokesman condemned 'the thoughtless behaviour of these people that has caused tremendous expense to the county and risk and trouble to the police, special constables and other volunteers' who had taken part in the search for the supposedly missing couple.

It would be pleasing to think that the Grishams were at least inconvenienced by the snow that returned to London on 8 February, with a storm lasting right through Saturday night. Five to ten inches fell on the capital and, 'owing to the lack of men, for the first time within memory' snowploughs were used in the City of London, and at Hornsey, Muswell Hill and Highgate. People were out 'skiing and tobogganing' at Boxhill. The blizzards swept on over the country, isolating many Shropshire villages and cutting off 'an area of 300 square miles' north of Market Rasen in Lincolnshire. In the uplands, ramblers and rock-climbers volunteered to help save buried sheep flocks, and the members of an RAF mountain rescue team, each carrying thirty pounds of food and 'guided by compass and radio', reached the village of Huggate on the Yorkshire Wolds, cut off for eight days. It took them three hours to cover just two miles.

On Monday 10 February, day-long power-cuts were imposed, leaving much of London and other towns and cities working by candlelight, hurricane lanterns and 'the grey winter light that filtered through the mist'. Many shops, cafes and restaurants closed, there were cuts in tram and train services and escalators in department stores and the London Underground were switched off. Most London theatres cancelled their matinees and the BBC announced that the Third Programme and all television broadcasts would be suspended 'for the duration of the emergency'. Several periodicals were ordered to cease publication until the power situation improved, and whether through altruism or in the hope of poaching their star columnists, some of the daily newspapers offered the periodicals a modest space within their pages. In the City, Whitehall and the West End, the power was left on, but a request for voluntary cuts 'appeared to be scrupulously observed', except at the Bank of England, which had its own generator, and the War Office, where a disapproving reporter noted that 'lights blazed from nearly every window'.

There was a brief thaw in the South that day but by Tuesday 11 February, temperatures had again sunk below zero and the snow was falling once more. This time the East Coast bore much of the brunt. The Great North Road was again blocked north of Alnwick, Cromer and Sheringham in Norfolk were cut off by six-foot drifts and all train and bus services in North Norfolk were brought to a standstill. No fish trains were able to leave Grimsby and 200 prisoners of war had to dig out a trainful of passengers for Peterborough stranded for twelve hours at Ludborough. Other trains were 'embedded in snowdrifts' near the Yorkshire coast. Fifteen men hauling a sledge battled through the snow to an isolated farmhouse at Settrington, East Yorkshire, from where they retrieved the body of a farmer, who had been dead for more than a week.

Second World War Halifax bombers were brought back into use, flying from Fairford in Gloucestershire to make food drops to Leek and Longnor in Staffordshire, where there had been no food deliveries for ten days. Villagers at Longnor marked out a 'black cross of soot' to help the pilot locate them. On 13 February, another mercy flight from Fairford to Butterton in Staffordshire ended in tragedy when the Halifax bomber making the food drop crashed on Grindon Moor, eight miles from Leek, killing all eight crew.

There was a brief respite from the snow around the middle of the month, but temperatures plunged even lower; 17 February was the coldest day in Falmouth since the nineteenth century. Councils and train companies seized the chance to clear blocked roads and railway lines. In the Northern Command area, 2,610 troops, together with 2,635 German POWs and 2,120 Poles were at work snow-clearing. In Bristol a thousand workmen laboured to clear the streets; as they finished, it began to snow again. Once more the snow spread right across the country, again closing roads that had only been cleared 'after days and nights of work'. In the Rossendale valley, where the snow was 'up to the level of the windows', some roads were blocked for five weeks. In Scotland, water supplies were threatened in Stirlingshire because the feeder streams to the reservoirs were all icebound.

At sea, ice-floes from the Rivers Scheldt and Rhine were sweeping along the Belgian coast, freezing together between Knocke and Blankenberghe into an ice-shelf ten inches thick and extending well out to sea. People walked on it up to 300 yards from the shore. Ice-fields had formed in the North Sea and drifted to within forty miles of the Norfolk Coast. Two Fishery Protection vessels sailed from Lowestoft on 18 February to investigate. They returned the following day warning that the ice was still drifting westwards and formed 'a menace to shipping' both in itself and because the ice was carrying away buoys marking wreck-sites and shipping channels between areas of uncleared mines from the war. A huge floe was also reported east of Great Yarmouth and over the next few days the ice drifted steadily closer to the coast. A Ministry of Agriculture and Fisheries official revealed that the sea temperature was two degrees below freezing point, and said that 'there is no record of anything like it being known before.' There were fears of 'much destruction' of stocks of herring and plaice because of the cold. Two trawlers were trapped in the ice before managing to escape and the Southern Railway announced the suspension of the Ostend ferry service 'until further notice' because of the danger from ice-floes.

19 February was the eighteenth consecutive day without sunshine at Kew, the longest sunless period ever recorded - a record that was to be extended to twenty-one days. The sun 'penetrated the clouds' briefly around noon, but the feeble light through the mist and murk was 'not strong enough to record on their instruments'. Even when it did eventually break through, it shone for a total of just seventeen hours in the whole month.

The next day, 20 February, the snow returned once more, spreading from the South-West to cover the whole country and continuing for most of the next two days. By the time the storm ended, it had left 'whole trains buried under drifts'. Miles of telephone and power cables had been brought down and many telegraph poles collapsed under the weight of snow, or of ice which was often two inches thick on the wires. The Settle-Carlisle railway line was again blocked by twelve-foot drifts and men laboured in vain to clear them.

Once more temperatures were in freefall, and a minimum of -21°C was recorded at Woburn in Bedfordshire early on 25 February. At Dungeness, Eastbourne and many other points around the coast, the sea was frozen up to one hundred feet from the shore, and at Whitstable in Kent, hundreds of people crowded the beach to watch 'masses of ice-floes extending for miles along the shore and over a mile out to sea'. In the harbour, barges and fishing vessels were icebound and as the tide ebbed, huge blocks of ice were left on the mud-flats. Pack-ice had formed in the estuaries of the Solent, Mersey and Humber. 'Practically the whole of the western seaboard of Wales is frostbound, and in the upper reaches of several North Wales rivers, ice-packs, some up to two feet deep, are floating downstream'. The Avon froze at Bristol for the first time in sixty years. People skated on the frozen lake in St James's Park in London, within sight of Buckingham Palace. Skaters were also out on the river at Evesham and the River Dee was icebound over a length of two miles. The Thames again froze at Windsor, and ice covering the water above Romney Lock had to be broken up. The Grand Union Canal was covered by a thick ice-sheet from Willesden to Paddington, leaving strings of barges icebound, and the ice on the Medway at Rochester was so thick that icebreaking tugs from the Admiralty had to be used to open a channel.

31 January 1947: The milk must get through.
A milkman in Cheam, Surrey, uses a sledge
to make his deliveries.

Snowed up in the Isle of Wight.

At teatime this afternoon, before we had drawn the curtains, I looked up from the Times crossword puzzle to see that while there was still a patch of pale cerulean high in the south-east corner of the window, everywhere else it was snowing. Instantly, just for a moment, I was restored to the magic world of childhood. Magic and childhood apart, I tend to associate snow with my youth, when I lived among the hills of the West Riding [of Yorkshire], and winter came much earlier - and much harder - than it does now, and three years out of four there would be heavy falls of snow around Christmas. (If we are all deceiving ourselves about this, then why is there so much snow on Christmas cards?) Even so, the only time I found myself completely snowed up was as late as February 1947. I was living in a fairly remote old house called Billingham Manor (said to be haunted) in the Isle of Wight. There was no nonsense about this snowed-upness. The one road to and from the house was blocked, utterly impassable; nothing could be delivered; the telephone lines were down; and for about a week we were cut off, sealed off, lost to the world. I passed the time writing a play over which I had been brooding for a month or two, and I had finished it when the road was clear again. It was called The Linden Tree and, with Sybil Thorndike and Lewis Casson leading the cast at the Duchess Theatre, it was an immediate "smash hit". But some of the credit must go to that astonishing snow storm in February.

JB Priestley.

Beautiful but deadly – hoar frost cloaks every twig and grass-stem.

A snowstorm sweeping Oxford Street in London. Normally one of the busiest streets in the world, it is eerily deserted, as shoppers once more stay at home, to the consternation of store owners.

For man and beast food was proving ever harder to find. Already scarce under rationing, many food items began to run out altogether. Supplies of milk, butter, meat, fish, and even bread were perilously low. To alleviate some of the shortages, the government had imported ten million tins of South African snoek, a fish hitherto unknown in Britain. Despite valiant attempts by Whitehall propagandists to convince the populace of its virtues, including the distribution of recipes for dishes like "Snoek Picquante", most were resolutely unimpressed.

Fresh food in shops, barns and warehouses was frost-blighted and winter crops like cabbages, sprouts, parsnips and turnips were buried feet deep beneath the snow and often frozen into the ground. Some farmers, like JH Moorhouse in Essex, even used pneumatic drills to dig parsnips out of their frozen fields. Farmers remained unable to plough their fields and plant their crops for three months, guaranteeing that the 1947 harvest would be one of the worst of the century.

Feed for livestock was also running out in many areas, and the losses of hill sheep were at catastrophic levels, 'higher than ever experienced'. Sheep buried by snow can last for days and even weeks, even eating their own fleeces to survive, but many died of starvation and cold, or were suffocated by wet snow when a thaw at last came, and those that were found alive were so weakened by their ordeal that huge numbers lost their lambs and many died

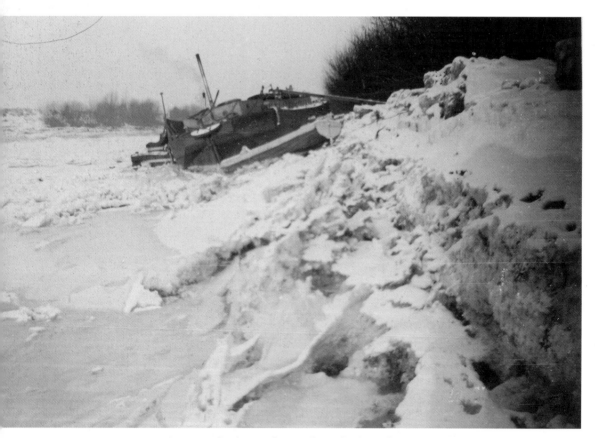

A tug and a barge frozen into the ice of a river. Tugs were used to try and keep waterways open, but they too sometimes became caught in the ice.

Two trains snowbound near Ribblehead on the Settle-Carlisle railway line.

themselves. 'Sheep are wandering over walls and have eaten the bark off trees. They stand about the porch of the village school waiting for scraps given them by the children. Two stray sheep which came in to feed with one flock were later found dead, one frozen to the barn door, the other with its head frozen into a watering trough where it had been to drink.' One farmer's cattle were so weak from lack of fodder that he 'had to lift them up each morning to feed them. Some households were near starvation point themselves.'

Over a thousand sheep were 'dead or dying on the moors around Ribblehead, in the then West Riding of Yorkshire, and three farmers each lost over half their flocks. A farmer from Mallerstang in Westmorland's upper Eden Valley, only moved onto his farm in the autumn of 1946, purchasing the stock of 500 ewes, all of which would have been carrying at least one lamb by the time the snow came. By the end of lambing time the following Spring, there were only 170 ewes and twelve lambs still alive. Some sheep in Lincolnshire had to endure a further hardship, for 'flocks of hungry crows are attacking sheep and some have been killed.' In the Lake District too, shepherds were 'now armed with guns to combat flights of carrion crows which are the latest menace to mountain sheep. Deprived by snow of their natural food, dozens at a time are swooping down on helpless sheep trapped in drifts, first tearing off their ears and plucking their eyes, then devouring the whole carcass'. Farmers in Merionethshire also reported large numbers of foxes 'driven by hunger from their mountain lairs to the lowlands, making daylight raids on sheep'. Around two million sheep were to die during the winter, 500,000 acres of wheat was lost and the frosts also destroyed much of the late potato crop, promising yet more hunger and misery for British families.

On the night of Tuesday 25 February yet another massive snowstorm swept the country. Northern Ireland, Eire, Scotland, Northern England, North Wales and the North Midlands were hardest hit. Scotland and England were completely cut off from each other as snowdrifts blocked every single cross-border road. The sleeping car express from London took ten hours to travel from Newcastle to Edinburgh. At one point the engine had to be uncoupled and 'by pushing and reversing, ploughed through ten foot drifts'. Newcastle and Sunderland were almost completely cut off. Two Greek steamers ran aground in the blizzard at Cullercoats and Whitley Bay in Northumberland, and the Belfast mailboat wrecked on the Isle of Arran. An avalanche sweeping 3,000 feet down a Merionethshire mountainside 'buried a farmer and his son in bed as it engulfed their farmhouse'. Their Dutch barn was carried 300 yards down the hill by the snow. By the time the storm blew itself out, there were drifts of twenty feet and more in Upper Weardale and North-East Durham, and all the surrounding dales.

On the last day of the month there was another 'very hard snowfall' in Kent and in Southend it snowed 'practically all day'. Villages on the Yorkshire Wolds were beginning their sixth snowbound week. Maximum temperatures had remained close to or below freezing throughout the month; in Oxford temperatures were below zero from 6pm on 10 February to 6am on the 26th. At Kew, chosen as the site of the Royal Botanic Gardens because of its gentle climate, on only two nights in the whole month did the temperature remain above freezing point. Deepening the winter gloom still further, Kew, Nottingham and Edgbaston all recorded no sun whatsoever on twenty-two of the month's twenty-eight days, and in some parts of Britain, snow fell on all but two days that month. Even in normally mild Dorset, there were only two nights without frost between 16 January and 11 March. Yet in a bizarre reversal, some places that would normally have expected the worst of winter weather had no rain or snow at all. A completely dry month in western Scotland is unusual at any time; in February it was unheard of, yet while the rest of the country suffered in the snow, in the West of Scotland the whole of February 1947 was dry and sunny.

For the rest of the country, commerce, industry and normal daily life were paralysed. In many areas people could only leave their homes and travel to their towns and villages by walking on the top of the snowdrifts, which by now were level with or higher than the wall-tops and hedges, and the tops of signposts and telegraph poles were often the only visible objects in a wilderness of white. Industrial production had fallen by a quarter, unemployment had reached two million and another two million were temporarily laid off because of power-cuts.

Despite the mountainous snowdrifts and arctic temperatures, valiant - and usually unsuccessful - efforts were still being made to break winter's grip. At Silloth in Cumbria, the stables at one farm were completely covered with snow, and the farmer could not get his horses out for two weeks. He had to leave his farmhouse by his bedroom window and then dig down through the drift in order to feed his horses. As he and his sons began trying to clear the snow from his gateway, an RAF snowplough came along the lane, but the snow was so thick that, after taking a run at it, the plough bounced back, leaving the driver dazed but uninjured. 'It is thought that, after limping back to Silloth Aerodrome, the plough never

Two men are dwarfed by a huge drift in front of their farmhouse.

SCHOOL

"No School Today". A small child trying not
to look too disappointed at the news.

moved again.'

Repeated attempts were made to clear the railway line over Stainmore between Bowes in County Durham and Kirkby Stephen in Westmorland, a vital link for farmers and their isolated communities, and between the Durham collieries and the mills of industrial Lancashire, blocked for over a month. The biggest obstacle was a snow-filled cutting at Bleath Gill, near Barras Station, just below the summit of the line. Attempts to clear the drifts using a train-driven snow plough failed - the plough became embedded in the snow and had to be dug out by hand. Gangs of hapless Italian prisoners of war, already held in miserable conditions in a disued Army camp on a windswept moor a few miles away, were compelled to dig out the cutting with picks and shovels, but every night there were fresh snowfalls and the wind also blew the excavated loose snow back into the cutting. After a fortnight's backbreaking work, they were farther away from the head of the cutting than they had been when they started.

Rail and Ministry of Transport officials then had the idea of using one of Britain's newest and most celebrated inventions - Sir Frank Whittle's jet engine - to clear the snow. Two powerful jets 'capable of developing 2,000 pounds pressure [each] and releasing hot gases at 1,000 miles an hour' were mounted on the rear truck of a train and backed up to the blocked cutting. The turbines began to revolve and the whine of the engine grew to a scream. The 'effects of the attack by these jet engines is spectacular. The blast sends up a huge cloud of fine snow particles, accompanied by great blocks of frozen snow which shoot

Just a group of three men, pausing from their snow-clearing duties... except that the snowdrift they're standing on reaches almost to the top of the telegraph pole behind them.

up to a height of about thirty feet. There was a fear that damage might be done to telegraph poles and wires along the track, but so far this has not happened. The assault, which at the moment is still experimental, opened on Saturday and would have been maintained throughout the night, but in the exceptional cold of Stainmore Summit, 1,370 feet above sea level, the electrical equipment of the jets froze and night work had to be abandoned.'

Initial reports of progress were optimistic. 'Already the progress made by these jet engines is equal to the thousands of man-hours worked by hundreds of troops and LNER relay gangs during the past month, in what must have been the worst blizzard conditions in the country.' However, 'ahead lies the worst part of the job. There, deep cuttings through rock have been filled, often to a depth of thirty feet. A train is buried; it had to be abandoned a month ago.'

Five days later it was clear that claims of the jets' effectiveness against hard-packed snow were very over-optimistic. An eyewitness recorded that 'jet engines developing a terrific, concentrated blast power have so far made no impression on the deep snow which for thirty-three days has choked the important mineral and passenger railway link. 'The frozen snow on the wastes of Stainmore Summit, which fills thirty cuttings on the highest stretch of railway in England... is snow pressed hard by its own weight, by hurtling winds and superficial thaws' and 'a thundering, screaming assault against the clean face of a six-foot drift composed of different layers of snow formed by a number of successive blizzards, was completely ineffectual. The result of a five minute assault was only 'a small section of the newest snow flung on to the adjacent track'. According to another eyewitness, a local man who lived at Barras just below the line, further attempts only demonstrated the jets' power in a wholly unintended way. Its brakes locked and streaming smoke, the train was propelled rapidly away from the cutting, leaving the snow-face undisturbed.

The jet engines were taken away and gelignite, mechanical diggers and drag-lines were used to try to shift the rock-hard snow. Blasting with gelignite 'has not moved material quantities of snow, though it has loosened it and made it easier to work. Grabs capable of lifting a cubic foot at a time have been abandoned because of the freezing up of the machinery. So hopes are turning once again to those unsung heroes of the desolation of Stainmore who have dug and redug for weeks. About a mile, with Barras Station at the centre, now separates the forces. Given favourable conditions (meaning no more snow and an absence of wind) the weekend might see a break through on a single line.' However, the winds undid much of each day's work by blowing excavated snow back in to the cutting, and further heavy falls added to the frustrations. Yet again, at the end of two weeks' hard work, they were twenty yards further from the end of the cutting than they had been at the start, and attempts to open the cutting were abandoned until the weather improved.

Any hopes that the arrival of March might herald a change to warmer weather were soon dispelled. The temperature remained stubbornly below freezing and further snowstorms continued to sweep in. There was at least some welcome news: coal stocks were 'improving' but, a government spokesman added, there was still 'a need for caution'. As if in confirmation, on 2 March, when power was restored to industries in London and the North for the first time in three weeks, the 'consequent heavy load' led to an immediate further round of power-cuts. On the same day, three men lost their lives in a snowstorm near Bangor Erris in Eire and on 4 and 5 March, there were further blizzards over most of England and Wales, with severe drifting. The snow was driven by fierce gales, leading to 'one of the wildest nights experienced for many years in the Channel', and the suspension of all shipping.

Sir Frank Whittle's new invention - the jet engine - being used to clear snow from railway lines. Although effective against soft, new-fallen snow, jet engines made virtually no impression on the hard-packed, frozen drifts blocking railway cuttings in the Pennines

Unexpectedly heavy falls of snow in the South trapped thousands on their way home from work in the evening rush-hour, and there was such chaos on Southern railways that the timetables were scrapped. Over a foot of snow fell in Birmingham, the depths of level snow reached five feet in upper Teesdale and the Denbighshire Hills, and the winds threw up drifts sixteen feet deep in the Pennines and Wales, and ten feet deep in the Chilterns. The South Coast, meanwhile, was affected by an ice storm, with heavy rain in Dover and Folkestone freezing as it fell. The weight of ice coating power and telephone lines brought them crashing down, buildings were covered in thick sheets of ice and icicles hung like stalactites from eaves and gutters.

Starving sheep were reported to be 'squatting' on the railway line near Goathland in Yorkshire and train drivers and firemen had to climb down from the footplate and 'push the

22 February 1947: Workers on Mr J H Moorhouse's farm struggle to get in the crop from hard-frozen fields. The men in the foreground are using a road-breaking pneumatic drill to lift parsnips, the others use picks and shovels.

sheep aside'. The postman had not been able to reach the 'seven cottages and eighteen inhabitants' of the remote Yorkshire Dales hamlet of Oughtershaw in Upper Wharfedale since 1 February and the fresh snowfalls meant that their isolation would be further prolonged. The only contact with the outside world had been achieved by villagers who had battled through the snow to Hubberholme and Buckden - several miles away, where food had been left for them by 'tradesmen who could penetrate no further. The goods were carried back to Oughtershaw 'on sledges and by hand' through sixteen-foot drifts. Despite those supplies, one of the villagers, Mrs EJ Speed, warned that 'the food position for both people and animals is serious. We were compelled to fell a tree in order to keep warm. We have no telephone, are seven miles from the nearest doctor and twelve miles from the nearest nurse.'

Temperatures plunged still further and there was one of the coldest March nights ever recorded with lows of -21.1°C in Braemar, Peebles and Houghall. The 'terrific chaos' continued into the next day when further heavy snowstorms caused fifteen foot drifts at

A train using its snowplough to blast its way through thick snowdrifts. It looks like an explosion – and dynamite was often used as the only means of clearing hard-packed snow in the worst affected areas.

Worcester, stranded more than 500 vehicles between Cheltenham and Burford and a further 300 between Cheltenham and Cirencester, and cut off a hundred villages in Leicestershire and Northants. By five that afternoon, not a single London to Birmingham route was passable and once more, said the AA, it was 'almost impossible to get from South to North'.

There were seven-hour delays on the London to Brighton line and a train limped into Euston Station, having taken twenty hours to travel there from Wolverhampton - it would almost have been quicker to walk. Buses were stranded halfway up the hills at Wimbledon, Putney and Crystal Palace, Rutland and Oakham were cut off and there was twenty-four hours continuous snow in Bedfordshire. At Brighton, eighty-three snowploughs and 900 men were 'employed all night clearing snow', and in Liverpool, where snow fell for twenty hours non-stop, 1,400 men worked all day trying to clear the city centre.

Passengers on a Manchester-bound train 'embedded' in a snowdrift at Tonfanau, Merionethshire, were taken to a nearby army camp for the night. Sailings from Holyhead were interrupted and 'the *Princess Maud* was fifteen hours late sailing'. At Whitby on the Yorkshire coast, spectacular icicles formed on the cliffs now 'reached down to the sea at high tide' and in the Yorkshire Dales, the Askrigg to Carperby road was reopened for the eleventh time that winter and then immediately blocked again. Elsewhere, the movement of coal was

An AA man uses his radio telephone to call for reinforcements.

A blizzard on a Glasgow street brings trams and buses to a grinding halt.

once more at a standstill and collieries in the Rhondda and West Wales shut down as absenteeism reached thirty-five per cent at some pits. It was even worse at Cannock Chase in the West Midlands, where fifty per cent of the miners were absent.

By the next day a huge swathe of Britain running north and east from Devon to the Scottish borders was completely 'snowed-up'. Attempts to use modern technology in snow-clearing again had mixed results. The 'use of heavy tanks swaying from side to side to break up the ice-top on snow drifts met with only limited success' and the 'use of a jet engine mounted on a tank in Derbyshire was of little avail against tightly-packed, frozen snow', though a Valentine tank fitted with two jet engines was successfully used to clear ten-foot drifts in Leicestershire.

The coal and power supply situation remained critical and in a bid to safeguard supplies, a Bill to extend British Summer Time until 2 November and reintroduce "Double Summer Time" from 13 April to 10 August had been speedily passed through the House of Commons on 5 March. Home Secretary Chuter Ede told the House that, although the move would produce 'almost negligible' estimated savings of 120,000 tons of coal in generating stations and 10,000 tons a year in gas works and domestic supplies, plus a further 20,000 tons from the reintroduction of Double Summer Time, it was necessary to spread the load on power

6 March 1947: Gangs trying to clear the snow away from the approaches to Smithfield Market, London.

stations and 'flatten' peak electricity demand, until the generation of power could be increased. The Bill would also make 'double dayshift working' possible.

There was further heavy snow in Yorkshire on 7 March when thousands of roads throughout the country remained completely blocked, and on 10 and 11 March, although much of the Midlands and the North had its first frost-free night for seven weeks, southern Scotland had its heaviest snowfall of the entire winter. The blizzards spread to the Scottish Highlands, where drifts of more than twenty-four feet deep were reported on 12 March. The armed services dropped supplies by helicopter to isolated Scottish farmsteads and villages, and helped to clear roads and railways. On the same day freezing rain fell in southern England and the Midlands, coating the lying snow in thick sheets of solid ice, and adding to the difficulties and dangers. In northern England it fell as snow. By 13 March, Carlisle was

6 March 1947: Pointless duty. A London policeman directing the largely non-existent traffic on the snowy streets outside St Paul's Cathedral.

Mountains of snow and ice ploughed from the roads were piled up at the kerbsides to await the spring thaw.

completely cut off from all sides and 'the heaviest snowfall of the year' had fallen in the North-East. Two US airmen survived a night on a Lake District mountain and three-mile tramp through snow and deep drifts after crashing their aircraft into the 2,000-foot summit of Black Combe. Both men were thrown clear by the impact as their aircraft was wrecked, but although not seriously injured, with visibility close to a white-out, they decided to stay on the mountain until the blizzard had ceased.

At the end of the next day, 14 March, many trains were still buried in drifts and only one rail route to Scotland was open - the LMS via Tebay - and only one cross-border road. The East Coast mainline was blocked in two places north of Newcastle near Acklington and Longhurst 'where two goods trains were embedded in deep drifts'. 600 passengers making for Scotland spent the night at Newcastle, 'curled up in railway carriages', while gangs of railway workers struggled even to clear a single track between Newcastle and Berwick. By the afternoon, enough of a way had been opened for two trains, preceded by a snowplough to have 'pushed their way through to Berwick, their passage being guided by hand-operated signals'. The line was then closed again and 'given over to the engineering section', which then had the task of clearing the up-line on which 'snow blocks remained so great that two goods trains, an empty coach-train and a snowplough were still buried in drifts'. The 5.10 from Glasgow to Stranraer was embedded in a thirty-foot drift thirteen miles from Stranraer, where it remained for two days, and the Newcastle-Carlisle line was also blocked by two derailments in the snow, one a coal-train, the other a goods train, causing 'the worst main-line hold-up on record in the North.'

Records were also tumbling on the roads, where the 'biggest road transport hold-up ever known' was occurring on Shap Fell in Westmorland. 'The worst section of the England to Scotland main road has a seven mile succession of the biggest drifts of the century and is likely to remain blocked for several days'. £1 million of machinery and supplies was held up in the jams and the towns of Kendal and Shap 'at each end of the impasse' were 'choked with hundreds of heavy lorries.' Police in neighbouring counties were stopping all vehicles from using the Shap route. Westmorland police advised drivers of stranded vehicles to 'go home by train, but while hundreds have abandoned their vehicles, many have received instructions from their employers that they must stay with their lorries to guard the loads.' As they sat shivering in their snowbound cabs, they would not have been amused to note that British Summer Time began that night.

Upland farmers, who had already lost huge numbers of sheep faced even further losses, with even those animals that had been rescued from drifts threatened by starvation. 'Convoys of lorries' stood ready to take fresh stocks of hay to farmers in Cumberland, Westmorland, Yorkshire, Durham and Northumberland, as soon as roads could be opened to them and one Bradford farmer, ID Grant of Wadlands Farm, Farsley, made a 300 mile round-trip to Norwich to buy four tons of hay for his stock. The journey took twenty-four hours, 'a hard trip,' said Mr Grant, 'but it was worth it; we could not see the sheep starve.'

It was almost winter's last flourish; the last widespread heavy snowfall in the North was on 15 March, though there were sporadic bursts until 17 March, by which time, snow had fallen somewhere in the UK on every single day since 22 January. 1947 had proved to be the worst winter of the century and perhaps the worst ever. No winter since records began has combined temperatures down to -21°C with such prodigious and relentless snowfalls. In three months a total of 210 cm of snow fell - well over six feet of level snow - and gales had raised drifts over forty feet deep in places.

As the last snow was still falling in the North, a dramatic change was already taking place in the South-West. A thick fog at dawn on the morning of 10 March indicated a sudden change in the weather. After three months of northerlies and easterlies, the wind had swung into the west and then the south-west, and mild air with a temperature of 7-10°C began edging over the frozen snowfields, its arrival signalled by dense fogs that reduced visibility to less than ten feet in places. The fogs were followed by heavy rain - on 10 March over an inch of rain fell right across the South from Cornwall to Sussex and temperatures rose rapidly with 10°C recorded at Penzance and Falmouth.

The effects of such warm and wet weather on the massive accumulations of snow were entirely predictable. Rainfall and meltwater could not penetrate the still-frozen subsoil and ran off in torrents. Streams and rivers rose rapidly and, unable to cope with the massive volumes of meltwater, soon burst their banks. The weather was now inflicting a different

form of torture and after thirty-six hours' torrential rain in Brixham, South Devon, boats were used to rescue people marooned on the upper floors of their houses by floods. By the evening of 11 March, vast areas of southern England were under water. As the warm air continued to spread northwards and eastwards, the Rivers Severn and Wye, swollen by meltwater from the Welsh mountains, flooded Herefordshire and Gloucestershire. The flooding spread steadily eastwards, tracking the thaw, and by 13 March, the rivers of East Anglia were also close to bursting their banks.

Landslides added to the problems. A large section of chalk cliff fell onto a bowling green at Ramsgate and a landslide at Buriton delayed trains from Waterloo to Portsmouth. Owners of farms and cottages in parts of Wirksworth, Derbyshire, were warned to evacuate their houses because the 'entire hillside above the town was moving over a distance of a quarter of a mile, after several landslips due to the effects of snow, severe frost and the subsequent thaw on the clay bed.' Despite this, 'most of the people refused to obey the warning and remained in their houses.' On 16 March a deepening Atlantic depression swept in, bringing storms, thunder and lightning and more torrential rain. There were sixty mile-an-hour gales over southern England with gusts peaking at over 100 miles an hour, damaging buildings and whipping the surface of the flood waters into waves like storm seas. By a cruel irony, in the midst of these oceans of water, over a million people in East London were without drinking water because of flooding at the Lea Bridge pumping station. Hundreds of houses were flooded as water spread over Hackney Marsh, Leyton and Walthamstow.

The gales killed at least fifteen people, including a man and wife killed in Abbey Road, St John's Wood in London, when their house 'was blown down'. Mr Edward Rotherham of the Post Office, Withybrook in Warwickshire, was killed when a tree fell on the car in which he was travelling with his wife and two small children, who were seriously injured. The top floor of a three-storey shop was blown off in Bristol, sending 'several tons of debris crashing into the street'. 'Suits were swept along a Birmingham main street after the shop front of an outfitter was blown in', there was 'extensive damage' in Bath and many windows smashed in Nottingham. A dredger broke adrift from a tug at Falmouth and went aground on St Just Point.

Large parts of Dublin were under water after 'a day of heavy rain which ended in a two-hour snowstorm'. 'Considerable damage' was done to 'fruit plantations' in the Vale of Evesham, the Severn valley was flooded for forty miles from Caersws to Shrewsbury with the floodwaters two miles wide in places. The Thames Valley was experiencing its worst floods in fifty years and vast areas were marked by 'unpathed waters, undreamed shores'. The waters in Oxford were 'gradually creeping into the city centre', Windsor station was closed because the tracks were submerged and the roads into the town were all flooded, with 'unbroken waters from Windsor to Weybridge'. Parts of Hampton Court Palace were under water, Eton High Street was flooded and Eton College closed. A mile and a half of the main road into Maidenhead was under water up to five feet deep and two Sherman tanks were used to tow 'from somewhere along the road, another tank which in turn had gone to someone's rescue the previous night and become immobile in soft mud.'

A horse-drawn cart carrying bales of rags is the only traffic on a snowbound Glasgow street.

March 15 1947. Five hundred houses and many other buildings were cut off when flood waters burst through the banks of the Great Ouse river at Bedford and swirled through the centre of town. Wagons carrying badly-needed coal were stranded in a siding.

The River Nene burst its banks at Northampton, and at St Neots in Huntingdonshire the gas works was flooded and all supplies to the town cut off. At its worst, the flooding was ten inches above the previous highest level, recorded in 1894. In East Anglia, the dykes collapsed, flooding most of Fenland. Troops were 'drafted into the Fen country for anti-flood work', but they could do little to stop the relentless flow of water through the breaches, and river levels continued to rise ever higher.

On 18 March, the Severn was fifteen feet six inches above its summer level at Worcester, only nine inches below the record 1886 level, and still rising. Shrewsbury was 'completely encircled, with only one high-level bridge above water', and milk, bread, mail and newspapers were being 'delivered by punt'. The Thames was now flooded from Windsor to Walton, six feet deep in places, and Staines, Wraysbury, Runnymede and Datchet were all cut

Householders in Trowbridge, Wiltshire wave from the top windows of their houses after the River Biss, swollen by melted snow, burst its banks and flooded the town.

Floodwaters cover the land near Chester. Only trees and the railway track stand clear of the flood but the rising waters bursting through the narrow arch of the tiny bridge, threaten to cut the line at any moment.

off by road and rail. Mr R Gray of Mixnan's Farm, Chertsey, drowned when his boat overturned.

Further north, the Trent burst its banks at Nottingham, flooding many houses to first floor level. When the floodwater reached the tidal reaches, it was held back by a Spring Tide, flooding the whole of the lower Trent valley. The River Derwent overflowed its banks 'all along its course from Malton to the point where it joins the Ouse, a distance of fifty miles', and thousands of acres were buried under water five and six feet deep. The Rivers Aire and Calder were joined by flood waters at Castleford in Yorkshire, and at Mexborough, a lorry driver, Thomas E Wakefield, 'stripped and swam one hundred yards in the flood waters of the River Don to rescue a dog from a kennel in which it had been swept downriver'.

While the lowlands were enduring floods, much of the high ground in the North was still snowbound. The road from Ingleton to Ribblehead in North Yorkshire was 'still blocked though it has been reopened fourteen times', and a cutting between Ribblehead and Dent on the Settle-Carlisle railway was 'completely filled by a block of ice thirty feet deep'. Only one road into Scotland was open and between Keswick and Grasmere in the Lake District 'police are not permitting any vehicle to proceed alone'. However there was relief for a number of railway travellers snowbound for five days on their way from Glasgow to Stranraer, who at last reached their destination.

By 19 March, apart from main roads in Kent, there was no county in England and Wales where roads were not affected by floods, snow or fallen trees. Gloucester was now flooded as the swollen waters of the Severn worked their way downstream. The depth of twenty-four feet seven inches was already 'four inches above the Great Flood of May 1886', and the record of twenty-four feet eleven inches, recorded in 1852, 'may be equalled today or tomorrow'. By the next day it had duly risen to a new record level of twenty-five feet, and it peaked a further three inches higher. Tewkesbury and Leominster were now isolated and all roads from South Wales to Birmingham were impassable. The River Wye at Hereford was at its highest for 155 years -'eighteen feet six inches in the St Martin's District' while 'a gauge below Hereford, erected to deal with any emergency up to twenty-one feet, is completely submerged. Hundreds of people are without water or gas supplies and hot meals are being taken to them from a British Restaurant'.

The Thames was 'well above' its record level. 'Inscribed on locks and walls of riverside inns and houses is the date 1894; when the waters have finally subsided, new record levels will have to be marked for this year.' The AA reported that 'of six main arteries radiating from London, only the Dover and Portsmouth roads were passable throughout their length. However, the floods did bring occasional advantages to the police. Three men escaping in a car after 'a smash and grab raid at Camberley' were hotly pursued by a police car which 'took up the chase at Staines Bridge, until at Hythe Lane, the fugitive car was stopped by flood water. Three men jumped out and dashed into the water', but two of them were at once apprehended.

Flood levels in the South and West began to fall after 20 March, but flood debris was still causing 'serious interference' to trains on London Transport, and rivers were still rising in Yorkshire and Eastern England. The Wharfe, Derwent, Aire and Ouse had now all burst their banks, inundating a huge area of southern Yorkshire. The Derwent was flooded for 'sixty miles from Ryedale to Wressle' and 'rose another foot at Stamford Bridge'. Mr Evelyn Walkden, MP for Doncaster, rushed to the House of Commons with a telegram he had received from the chairman of Bentley District Council: "Bentley flooded. 1000 people isolated without food for 24 hours. Small boats useless owing to powerful currents. Power-driven boats essential for food distribution and evacuation of people. Help must be here Thursday morning. Position desperate." At midnight that night, the War Office announced that two Army "Ducks" - amphibious vehicles - were on their way to Bentley from Aldershot.

Over one hundred square miles of Fenland were now under water and Spring Tides were having 'a detrimental effect'. On the roads, lorries laden with salvaged furniture travelling away from the flooded areas, passed 'WVS and Salvation army canteens coming into the area' to provide food and hot drinks for those stranded or at work fighting the floods. The bells of Crowland Abbey were rung as a flood warning when a forty-yard-wide breach occurred in Deeping High Bank. The Lower Trent flooded thousands of acres around Gainsborough. People worked by 'car lamps and searchlights' in an unavailing attempt to stem the waters rushing through the ever-widening gaps in the banks of the Ouse. At Ely an attempt was made to close a 150 foot gap in the banks with a 200 foot Bailey Bridge, but 'the idea has now been abandoned'.

A thousand men were at work sandbagging parts of the Ely to King's Lynn road to prevent '20,000 acres of rich agricultural fenland being flooded'. The effort was largely unsuccessful; on 23 March 'another 12,000 acres of Fenland were flooded when a culvert between Ely and King's Lynn burst', and the next day 'flood waters west of Ely were pounding in waves' against the banks of the New Bedford River and undermining them'. On the highest of the Spring Tides at Boston in Lincolnshire, 'a 25-foot wall of seawater in the tidal estuary held up the fresh water. For the next two hours, hundreds of workers fought ceaselessly to buttress the danger spots'. Meanwhile, a ship was 'brought round from King's Lynn to block a breach in the bank of the River Wissey.' 'The spreading waters have already reached ground floor windows of hundreds of houses and many bridges have collapsed. Most of the cattle have been rescued but it is feared that potatoes and cattle feed will be destroyed.'

In Yorkshire the floods were the worst in 250 years and in York the worst ever recorded. On 24 March the river was at seventeen feet above the normal level - six inches higher than the floods of 1894 - and still rising, and the city was 'in danger of losing its supply of water and electricity'. Townspeople were warned to boil all water. Downstream from York, the town of Selby was almost completely under water. Only the ancient abbey and the streets around the market place escaped inundation.

On 25 March the Lord Mayor of London opened a national fund 'for the relief of distress caused by the floods' to which the Government at once contributed £1 million. A huge number of organisations and individuals added their contributions. The States of Jersey contributed £5,000 and the American Red Cross sent 'fifty tons of soap, one thousand brushes and a thousand gallons of disinfectant'. Among individual donors, 'Mr E Cross of Aberdeen, who won £61,456 in a football pool, has given £500.' To no one's surprise, the month of March proved to be the wettest on record.

If the winter had at last ended, the Minister of Agriculture called the effects of the prolonged snowfall followed by the floods 'a disaster of the first magnitude', and the crisis was exacerbated by continuing fuel and food shortages in the aftermath of the war. This extraordinary year then saw one of the hottest and most prolonged drought summers on record. Temperatures climbed into the mid-thirties Celsius and apart from occasional ferocious thunderstorms triggered by the heat, there was no significant rain until well into autumn. Kent went fifty days without a drop of rainfall at one point, and October and November were the driest, sunniest and warmest on record in many parts of the country.

It was a golden summer for English cricket - Denis Compton and Bill Edrich both plundered well over 3,000 runs from the sun-baked pitches, with Compton's totals of 3,816 runs and eighteen centuries never likely to be equalled - but the drought did further damage to an already crippled harvest and led to severe food shortages and rising discontent among a war-weary population.

The most turbulent year of British weather ever recorded then concluded with one final spectacular: a thunderstorm on Christmas night that saw hailstones 'as big as marbles' fall across large parts of the South.

Farmers struggled to fodder their sheep and millions were lost.

Snow level with the roof.

When the "Great Snow" of 1947 began to fall, Rose Walmsley was living with her husband Fred and their two year-old daughter Heather at the isolated Newhouse Farm, 1,000 feet above sea level in Upper Wharfedale.

'I can remember it as if it were yesterday. It hadn't been too bad a winter, and when it got through to February we thought we were over the worst of it. Then it started one Sunday. On the Friday we'd killed a pig and on the Saturday we salted it. On the Sunday, Fred was busy sawing wood, when suddenly the sky clouded over and the snowstorm came out of the north.

It was fine, powdery snow, whizzing round and swirling all over the place. It just kept on snowing and the terrific wind never stopped. By Tuesday the snow had blown level with the roof at the back of the house, forming a tunnel between the building and the drift. At the other side you couldn't even see the front door or windows.

I let Fred out of the back bedroom window into the snow tunnel using pig blocks - he was terrified I was going to drop him! He then forced his way round to the front and started to dig down to the outside door, making seven deep steps in the snow.

On the Wednesday things improved a bit and the sun came out. We knew we had to get Heather down to Grassington where she could safely stay with Fred's parents. All we had was a horse and a hay sled, so what we did was to line a dustbin with big hessian sacks. We then put Heather inside, tied the bin to the sled and Fred set off. I shall never forget the sight of this little figure with just her gloves visible as she clung on to the sides.

The snow had blown right over the tops of the gates and walls and it was freezing so hard that it was very crisp. It supported the weight of both the horse and the sled. Fred simply set off in a straightish line and eventually got down to Grassington. There were no tractors or snowploughs, so he picked up some meat and vegetables to leave at the hospital on the way back. They were running short and were right glad to see him. Finally he landed back; he had to leave the mare in the snow tunnel as there was nowhere else for it.

Soon afterwards it dulled in and started to snow again. It carried on like this for weeks on end, with two or three days of blizzard and then a bit of sunshine before more snow came. But there was never enough sun to start a thaw and so the drifts got higher and higher.

The wind never let up neither. It was what Fred called a lazy wind - it would blow through you rather than round you. It searched out every crack, forcing the snow through the sash windows. There was even a drift in the passageway formed by snow coming through the front door keyhole.

We had ten cows tied up inside the barn and each day it took us hours to muck out. Everything had to be carried by climbing up and over the snow. Then we had to find the trough so that we could bucket water to the cattle. Each night the drifts had blown over it. We also had to feed the horse which was still living inside the snow tunnel.

The biggest job of all was getting fuel inside the house. Fortunately we'd plenty of wood and we heaped the logs right up the chimney so that we had a roaring fire to keep us warm. We kept the boiler in the back kitchen full of water by opening the window and getting shovelfuls of snow, although it's amazing how much we needed.

It's a good thing we'd killed the pig just before the snow started as it meant we were all right for meat. The pork froze solid in the pantry and kept for weeks on end. We rolled the sides up for bacon and I cooked spare rib in all sorts of different ways. Often I would casserole it slowly in the fireside oven - it smelt wonderful and tasted delicious.

Fred always believed in keeping enough of everything to last a month. We had lots of oats and so had porridge every day. We also had plenty of spuds and were all right for turnips, which had been got in to be chopped up for the cows. There was lots of flour in eight-stone bags, so Fred brought back a great block of yeast and I made bread. We also made our own butter and had eggs from our own hens, so we didn't do too bad considering.

It was April before the sun at last started to melt the snow and lambing time that year was dreadful. Even then it took ages for it all to go and there was plenty still around in June. Heather was away for eight or nine weeks before we dare bring her back.

We've had other bad winters but nothing like 1947. Today it's very different if it snows hard. Farms have electricity and tractors with a bucket up front. All we had were oil lamps and hand shovels.

It was a winter I shall never ever forget - I didn't see another woman from February to May.'

PART IV

The Coldest Winter – 1962-63

If 1947 was the snowiest, the winter of 1962-63 was to prove the coldest, not just of the twentieth century but as far back as 1740. A cold snap beginning on 8 November 1962 ushered in one of the worst November blizzards ever recorded. Over the weekend of 16-17 November, gales gusting to eighty-five miles an hour hit the Scilly Isles and the sleet that covered the islands fell as snow over the British mainland, with heavy drifting in the fierce winds. Roads were blocked and traffic dislocated as far south as Somerset, Devon and Cornwall.

There was a brief respite, then on 3 December dense fog blanketed eighteen counties in England and Scotland. London Airport was closed, with freezing fog reducing runway visibility to fifty yards. Three Boeing jets from New York were diverted and all outgoing flights were grounded. Conditions were even worse in parts of London, with five yard visibility reported from Wimbledon and Malden, and "nil" visibility in the Wembley area.

The following day the fog persisted with a toxic cloud of "smog" - a mixture of smoke from coal fires and sulphur dioxide - returning to the streets of London and Britain's other big cities, the worst since the 'Great Smog' of 1952. Concentrations of smoke and sulphur dioxide were already nine and five times the normal average respectively. Four lives were lost in crashes in the fog. The worst incidents were multiple pile-ups on fogbound motorways, but buses and trains were also involved in collisions. Thousands of cars were stuck in jams on the North Circular Road, many drivers abandoned their vehicles, 'many others halted behind, unaware that they had done so'. The Duchess of Kent, with her five month old son, was due to fly from Stansted to Hong Kong, but got no further than the outskirts of North London before abandoning the attempt and returning to Kensington Palace.

The only aircraft to land at London Airport all day was 'a twin-engined Ministry of Aviation Varsity Aircraft from the Blind Landing Experimental Unit at Bedford', seizing the chance to test their equipment. BEA alone cancelled 82 flights from Heathrow and though at one time more than 1,000 frustrated would-be passengers crushed into 'final departure lounges', all were turned back. Hundreds of rush-hour passengers on the 5.06 pm train from Liverpool Street to Chingford 'had to get out and walk' when it derailed at St James's Street station, Walthamstow. A farmer from Islip near Oxford was killed when his tractor was hit by a diesel train on a fogbound level-crossing and twelve people were injured in Bradford when

The snow turned the normally bustling centre of Bradford, Yorkshre, into a ghost town.

a car left the road in the fog and ran into a bus queue. Thirteen people were hospitalised after two London Transport buses collided at Manor Park, and a woman drowned in the Rochdale Canal at Failsworth, Manchester, after 'missing her way while crossing a bridge'.

By the next day, 5 December, the Air Ministry was reporting that smoke and sulphur pollution was 'as great as in the Great Smog of 1952'. Ford at Dagenham sent their workforce home at 2pm that day, though forty percent of the dayshift had failed to turn up for work anyway. Shipping in the Port of London was at a standstill, the Clyde was also closed to shipping and London Airport was again closed. Fans of Tottenham Hotspur travelled to Glasgow for the European Cup Winners Cup tie against Rangers found when they arrived that the game had been called off because of the fog. Bus services were suspended and London Transport ordered drivers to make for the nearest garage at once. Scotland Yard announced that there had been twenty-eight sudden deaths in London that day, 'the usual figure is six to eight a day'. There were other deaths caused by the fog. A fireman whose goods train had developed an engine failure at Kentish Town West plunged forty feet to his death from a viaduct as he walked up the line to lay detonators on the track as a warning to other trains.

On the following day, Thursday 6 December, it was reported that cases of pneumonia had trebled in Glasgow since the smog began. Thirty people, mostly elderly, had been admitted

Only foot-traffic is moving as a long line of stranded vehicles wait for some sign of gritters.

to St James's Hospital in Leeds, suffering from chest complaints and Mr R Dalley, Leeds City Analyst, said that sulphur dioxide levels in the atmosphere were now the highest ever recorded, exceeding those in London during the Great Smog. Concentrations of smoke were now ten times, and sulphur dioxide fourteen times normal levels. 'There is no doubt that without the Clean Air Act of 1956, the conditions would have been much worse than 1952', Mr Dalley said. A further thirty sudden deaths were reported to London's Metropolitan Police that day, taking the total since midnight on Monday to ninety.

All forms of transport were seriously disrupted and thousands of drivers simply abandoned their cars and walked. One Bradford man drove to a party hanging out of the window as he tried to see the white line in the middle of the road, while his passenger leant out of the other side trying to spot the kerb. When they eventually reached their destination, after taking forty-five minutes to drive three miles - longer than it would have taken to walk - they discovered that the party had been cancelled because of the fog.

At times visibility over the whole of the Greater London area was less than five yards, and several leading London stores complained that the fog was keeping Christmas shoppers away, with turnover well down. London Airport remained closed, and chaos on road and rail continued. All London buses were again halted for the night at seven that evening. A railway

A motorist making the seemingly futile attempt to extricate his car from a queue of snowed-up and abandoned vehicles.

shunter was killed and three workers injured when two empty trains collided at Gillingham and half the passengers on the twelve-coach 8am train from London to Brighton were stranded at Streatham when the train 'broke in two and the second six coaches slowed down and stopped without the passengers realising that they had been left behind.' The loose carriages were eventually pushed into Streatham Common station by the next London to Brighton train.

On the morning of Friday 7 December, a Middle East Airlines Comet taxied up and down the main runway at London Airport with the pilot running the engines 'at high power'. The heat from the engines cleared a path through the fog for a few minutes, during which the Comet took off, bound for Rome and Beirut. It was the first aircraft to take off at Heathrow in four days. A plane carrying the 79 year-old Princess Alice also took off successfully from Bovingdon, Hertfordshire, in ninety yard visibility but was then forced to turn back by fog over Holland. By then the fog had largely cleared over London Airport and she landed safely and then travelled to Kensington Palace by car. She considered her options over a spot of lunch and then set off again, travelling by car and boat-train from Harwich to the Hook of Holland. The four days of fog at London Airport had caused the cancellation of 300 BEA services at a cost of £150,000.

What was to prove to be the last of the old-style smogs was over, but 'the appearance of cars left standing unprotected during the past few days is sufficient proof that curtains and

A stranded "half-timbered" Morris 1000 Traveller on a road near Bournemouth.

the like will have collected their fair proportion of London's combustion products - including acid, which is better washed out than left in.' The Times of 8 December editorialised that '"pea-soupers" and "London Particulars" were undoubtedly worse cursed by blackness, but they were not any worse - and some would say they were better - in respect to lethal fumes.' Dr JA Scott, the London County Council's Medical Officer, later estimated that the capital's total deaths from respiratory problems caused by the four-day smog had been 340 people - other estimates ranged as high as 1,000 - and The Times went on to call for action to remove toxins from the air, claiming that smokeless zones were 'in a sense confidence tricks', leaving air apparently cleaner but full of toxins like sulphur dioxide. That drew a furious response from the Society for Clean Air, which deplored 'hysterical, hasty and ill-considered press statements'.

After that unpleasant prelude, the winter of 1962-63 began in earnest at Christmas. On Christmas Eve more fog and black ice caused thirty-five accidents in Leicestershire alone; two people were killed and more than twenty injured. The newspapers reported a record Christmas 'rush to the sun from London Airport, with 60,000 departures since last Thursday'. They left just in time...

A belt of rain over northern Scotland turned to snow as it moved south, giving Glasgow its first white Christmas since 1938 and Guernsey its first since 1919. Temperatures plummeted. Kew had its coldest Christmas since 1944, Gatwick, Hurn, Abingdon, Ross-on-Wye and Cardiff all recorded -9°C in the early hours of Boxing Day and in Birmingham dropped to -11°C. Ground temperatures were even lower; it was -15° C at Birmingham, and snow then falling on already frozen road surfaces caused traffic chaos, with the AA reporting that all roads from the Midlands to southern Scotland were 'very dangerous'. Not to be outdone, the RAC added that 'Drivers are slipping about as if they were learners on skates.' By sunset on Boxing Day heavy snow was falling all along the South Coast of England and even in the Scilly Isles.

By the following day, 27 December, the North was 'gripped by Arctic conditions', there was two inches of snow in the Channel Islands and it was a foot deep across much of southern England. Roads over the Mendips were closed and the London to Hastings road had 'deep drifts in several places' and, said the RAC, cars were sliding off the roads 'like spinning tops'. Letters were scattered all over a Lowestoft pavement when a bus skidded off an icy road into a post-box. Many flights were cancelled - Gatwick had almost a foot of snow on the runways - and rail delays made thousands of Londoners late as they returned to work after the Christmas break. Eire was also badly affected with Dublin roads 'hazardous'.

A fresh blizzard over South-West England and South Wales on 29 and 30 December produced snowdrifts up to twenty feet deep. There was heavy snowfall in the North and Scotland too, with the RAC reporting 'deteriorating road conditions'. Villages were cut off, roads and railways blocked, telephone wires and power cables brought down. Thousands of sheep, ponies and cattle were buried under the snow.

Seventy-one passengers from two coaches were trapped overnight at the Clay Pigeon Cafe at Warden Hill near Evershot, Yeovil. Among the passengers were a dozen children and a month-old baby girl, Tracie Gallagher, from Birmingham. A local farmer provided her mother with a cardboard box as a crib, where the child, wrapped in blankets, spent the night. They were still trapped twenty-four hours later, though 'a man on skis' had got through with some baby food. A snow plough was reported to be on its way, but the cafe owner said there was 'little hope' of it being able to reach them that day. Another two parties of passengers stranded at Lee Mill near Plymouth, were rescued by police in mid-morning after a frozen night in their coaches. Yet another pair of buses, carrying twenty-five passengers, were stranded by twenty-foot drifts on the Blandford to Salisbury Road in Dorset before eventually being rescued by a farmer 'with a tractor and horsebox'. Farmer Mr Charles Burt, his wife and their four small children, spent all night in their car after becoming stuck in a snowdrift on the Isle of Wight. After eleven hours 'huddled in the back', they were found by council workers, who dug them out.

A baby boy was born in a snowbound ambulance at Praze on the Helston to Redruth road in Cornwall, and a helicopter dropped yeast and milk to the bakery at Dartmoor Prison where supplies were running perilously low. Seventy railway enthusiasts had their enthusiasm tested to the limits after being trapped on a train at Tavistock all Saturday night. Police took food to them on Sunday and eventually they struggled through the snow on foot to an emergency rest centre set up by the Women's Voluntary Service. The night express from Penzance to London Paddington left on time at 8.50pm but 'had such a struggle through Cornwall' that it didn't leave Plymouth until five o'clock the following morning. Frozen points then delayed it further at Bristol and it eventually arrived six hours fifty minutes late. Troops were called in to clear snow from the sidings at Willesden to release rolling stock for the Monday morning rush hour, and many Southern Region lines were blocked, with Orpington closed until Sunday afternoon.

An ambulance on the way to pick up an expectant mother at Farningham, Kent, was stuck in several feet of snow for nearly six hours before two snowploughs managed to free it. An RAF helicopter rescued four people trapped all night in a car at Blackmore Gate on Exmoor

Commuters inching over the Clifton Suspension Bridge in Bristol.

and a young mother-to-be, Angela Christmas, was rescued unconscious but alive after being trapped all night with her husband in a six-foot drift at Crockenhill, Kent. PC Peacock of Swanley Police rescued them as he was returning home from night duty.

However, several lives were lost because of the snow. A sixty-five year-old railway worker, John Warren of South Benfleet, was killed by a train as he tried to clear snow and ice from frozen points, a sixty year-old milk roundsman, William Starkey, collapsed and died while making deliveries in the snow, and a husband and wife, Arthur and Daisy Barber, were found dead in their car after being trapped by drifts on Osmington Hill, Weymouth. Their daughter, Mrs Sheila Reed, her seven year-old son, Ian, and Thomas Cumbes of Dorchester, who were trapped with them, all survived.

On New Year's Eve, the one month-old baby, Tracie Gallagher, and her mother were among sixteen passengers - the others all elderly or sick - rescued from the Clay Pigeon Cafe by a Royal Naval helicopter flying from Portland in Dorset. All the other passengers were left behind, but were being rescued ten at a time by a farmer's tractor and trailer, running 'a shuttle service' to Cattistock, from where coaches took them to Dorchester. At Denton Mains, near Gilsland in Cumberland, twenty people were trapped for fourteen hours in two service buses. They were only 500 yards from a farm, but in the blinding snow, no one realised that, and when farmer Thomas Graham eventually discovered them, 'Everyone in the bus looked ill'.

Troops were used in many areas to open roads and rescue stranded people. Soldiers from

Edinburgh to London sleeping car train snowed up near Dent station.

the Wessex Brigade depot at Honiton and the RASC at Yeovil were brought up in a special train and worked through the night in an effort to clear the blocked railway line between Tavistock and Okehampton. Men of the Gurkha Regiment - who presumably knew a thing or two about snow - cut their way through 'a big snowdrift' near Amesbury, Wilts, where 'sick and old people were marooned'. Sappers from Chatham used bulldozers to clear roads in Kent and Sussex, and on Salisbury Plain an Army Operations Room was set up to co-ordinate rescue missions to isolated farms. Despite the best efforts, Weymouth, Bridport and many other areas were still completely cut off by 'high drifts, icy floods and abandoned vehicles'. As night fell on this, the last day of 1962, it was still snowing heavily and almost the whole of Britain was covered by snow.

It was not going to be a happy new year for farmers. Farm dairies were 'overflowing for lack of churns' and farmers had to pour thousands of gallons of uncollected milk down the drain. In Sussex, ten thousand gallons of milk was standing at the roadside, waiting in vain for tankers to collect it, while the Milk Marketing Board had begun making hardship payments from an emergency fund. While there was a glut of milk on the farms, doorstep deliveries in London and the Home Counties were being threatened by a shortage of milk and of bottles to put it in. A spokesman for National Dairies warned 'unless customers make efforts to hand in empties, there could have to be reduced supplies.' London's milk supplies were given a temporary boost by 'a switch of thousands of gallons from Cheshire, the Midlands and East Anglia', but the position remained critical.

Farmers in the Fens and East Anglia who had 'already lost thousands of pounds worth of celery because of the frost', were fighting to save 175,000 tons of sugar beet, valued at £1 million, which was frozen into the ground. The Cantley sugar beet factory 'faced closure' if supplies of beets did not arrive soon. Tens of thousands of animals were buried by snowdrifts. Thousands of sheep and more than two thousand ponies were trapped on Dartmoor and the Horses and Ponies Protection Association issued an appeal 'for the rescue of the animals'. Whipsnade Zoo was cut off and keepers struggled on foot through twelve-foot drifts to feed the animals. Human food supplies were also threatened. A spokesman for the National Federation of Fruit and Potato Traders, perhaps shedding a few crocodile tears, announced that prices of vegetables and many fruits had 'shot up' since the snow began and would reach a peak later that week.

At London Airport, two runways had now been cleared, but seventeen BEA Comets, Vanguards and Viscounts were still grounded by three-foot drifts, more than twenty-four hours after the last snow had fallen there. A Ministry of Aviation spokesman claimed, 'We are clearing the taxi-ways and terminal aprons as fast as we possibly can,' but airline chiefs were furious at the delays. Meanwhile a spokesman for British Railways Western Region was praising its workers who had walked to work, 'many trudging distances of from three to eight miles. Two teenagers in the Enquiry Office at Bristol stayed on duty from 9am to 10.30 pm on Sunday, and then walked home. A snow plough crew remained on duty for eighteen hours.'

The gales that were still piling up drifts on the high ground, also brought further problems off the coast. Heavy seas backed by the fierce winds did 'widespread damage' at Paignton in Devon. 'A thirty-two-foot naval cutter was dashed against the West Quay and sank. Small boats were damaged and sea-front kiosks blown over.' The motorship *Egton* broke her moorings in the River Wear at Sunderland. Two helicopters of 22 (Search & Rescue) Squadron at RAF Chivenor, Devon, spent ten and a half hours - from first light until after dark - flying rescue missions and food drops to isolated areas. During four sorties to take food to Lynton, 'the wind was so strong that the helicopters were 'flying sideways like crabs'. Gales also caused severe damage on land, leaving 'a trail of destruction over the Macclesfield area'. Only one route from Macclesfield to Bollington remained open as 'trees fell like ninepins'. The winds also toppled the 200-foot mill chimney of Firgrove Mill in Rochdale. It crashed across the Rochdale Canal and tore a hole through the wall of J & J Makin's paper mill, 'where the night-shift was working. Two workmen ran for their lives.'

A road was closed in Royton, Lancashire, after 'a large corrugated iron engineering workshop' collapsed, and 300 people were evacuated from the Ritz Cinema in Stockport after 'large roof tiles' were torn off by the wind. A chimney stack tore a twenty-foot hole in the roof of a wines and spirits firm in Chesterfield, gable ends collapsed in several towns, and shop windows were blown in. Twelve Euston to Glasgow expresses were delayed after 'the stay-wires' of a telegraph pole snapped in the gales and it 'swayed over the line'. An Air Ministry spokesman helpfully explained that 'in this type of easterly airstream, funnel effects caused by local land contours can produce these freak winds'.

Water from a burst pipe seeped through three floors of 'a large furnishing store in Hammersmith' causing hundreds of thousands of pounds damage, and there were further human tragedies and near-tragedies. Roadmen found Mrs Donna Douglas, 'Cinderella in the pantomime at the Empire Theatre, Sunderland', and Mr Charles William Brown of Railway

Hotel, Miller's Dale, Derbyshire, unconscious in a car buried by snow at Carter Bar on the A68 at Jedburgh. The car engine was still running and 'the occupants overcome by fumes'. Both had to be given oxygen and were very fortunate to survive. A sixty year-old woman, Mrs Wanda Zakrzewska of Shalbourne near Marlborough in Wiltshire, was less lucky. She had taken her dog for a walk in the snow and was later found dead 'in a trench near her home'. Her unharmed dog was still sitting next to her body. A railway signalman, fifty-five year-old Albert Heddington, collapsed and died as he trudged through the snow to work at Greenfield goods yard near Oldham in Lancashire. And George Rose, forty-six, of Tunbridge Wells, also collapsed and died while shovelling snow from the steps of the Rehoboth Baptist Chapel.

The new year had begun as the old one had ended, with heavy snow, described by Gordon Manley, Professor of Geography at Bedford College, London University, as 'the worst over southern England for eighty-two years.' In the hundred years for which records were available, he said, the only worse year was 1881, when on January 18, 'there was a drift fifteen foot deep in Oxford Circus' in the heart of London. More than 200 classified roads and thousands of minor roads were 'strangled by slush, snow and ice' according to the RAC, despite the efforts of 'more than 1,000 snow-clearing appliances' in England and Wales and, said an AA spokesman, 'the only thing going up the M1 is snow'.

Frederick Bridges, licensee of the Forest Inn, Hexworthy in Devon, shared his last loaf of bread with fifteen unexpected guests, including a baby, snowed in with him at the inn since Christmas. 'We ran riot over Christmas, never expecting a big snowfall like this and made heavy inroads into the food... An emergency call has gone out for bread-mix and baby food, and a helicopter from Plymouth will try to land supplies of these early this morning.' The forty-strong population of the village were hard at work making a cross in the snow to guide the helicopter in. And weathermen at the Ministry of Aviation weather station on Great Dun Fell in Westmorland - who might, perhaps, have been expected to predict their own plight - were rescued after being snowbound there for four days. A relief party 'walked five miles up the 2,800-foot fell through the blizzard to reach them'.

A surgeon at St Thomas's Hospital, London, Richard Boggon, was meanwhile preparing for an even longer "mercy dash" after being summoned to the island of St Helena in the South Atlantic, where ten people were seriously injured in a bus crash on a mountain road. The island's doctor desperately needed the help of a surgeon since 'several of the injured on the island need major operations including amputations', and the government arranged for Dr Boggon 'a bachelor' to fly out. He had been up until 4am at a New Year's Eve party, but since receiving the call at ten the following morning, he had been 'racing around like mad', collecting drugs and other medical supplies.

The bad weather was welcomed by servicemen who 'have been sent telegrams telling them not to come back from their leave yet' and 12,700 car workers in the Midlands were sent home because of the snow, though 'at least another 3,000 failed to turn up at all.' Airline staff at London Airport were helping to clear away the drifts from 'parked airliners' and de-icing teams worked from one frozen aircraft to another, but BEA still cancelled thirty-two flights. North Londoners had to shiver in the cold without electricity for two hours as a series of power failures blacked out Finsbury, Muswell Hill, Barnet, Hornsey and Hendon. A spokesman for the Eastern Electricity Board said that the breakdowns were caused by 'overloading of low voltage cables'. He added the unsurprising news that 'because of the cold weather, people were switching on all their heating appliances.'

14 January 1963: The frozen fountains in Trafalgar Square look like a huge iced cake. Hungry pigeons scavenge for food left by the RSPCA.

The following day, 2 January, 'some new deadly ingredients were added to the weather recipe: a freezing drizzle which iced up windscreens, a freezing fog which cut visibility to nil in places and "black ice" on roads newly cleared of snow'. The railways were perilous too. The three-man crew of a 600-ton coal train jumped to safety into a snowdrift seconds before the train crashed at Bradford after sliding through a set of points on the icy rails. The runaway engine 'ploughed into a concrete stop-block, leapt into the air, shot thirty yards along a platform, wrecked a steel water tank and stopped perched over a thirty-foot drop.'

Snowbound villages in the Cotswolds suffered power-cuts as a main transmission line iced up and at London Airport the freezing drizzle hampered the work of de-icing crews, causing fifty flights to be cancelled. An eight year-old boy, Matthew Lowe, of Staveley in Derbyshire, drowned when skating on a park lake, and after searching for two hours Bedford police frogmen found the body of 'a man in his early twenties' after he had fallen through the ice while skating on the Great Ouse in Bedford. A fifty-one year-old Cambridgeshire woman, Mrs Joan Chadwick, was also found dead 'in a snow-covered hut three miles from her home'. However the thirty-three children and thirty staff at the Beatrix Potter Children's Nursery at Knoyle, near Shaftesbury in Dorset, were pronounced to be all well, despite being 'marooned for several days'.

In an attempt to pick up 'an eighty year-old sick woman' from Princetown on Dartmoor, a Whirlwind helicopter from RAF Chivenor was 'forced to fly backwards out of a blinding fog' when only 150 yards from the village. Another helicopter later succeeded in making the rescue and the woman was taken to hospital in Tavistock. From Sussex to Devon, helicopters dropped 'coal, medical supplies, milk and food, spare parts and fodder to isolated settlements and farms'. An officer at RAF Chivenor said they were 'now having to run a twenty-four hour, round-the-clock emergency service. We are picking up people all over the county who can only be described as being half-frozen to death, and then rushing them to hospital. Some snowdrifts here are now up to twenty-four feet deep,' and police at Barnstaple said that many of the sheep and ponies buried by the snow 'must now be dead'.

The weather later that day can only have deepened the drifts still more as 'one of the fastest moving blizzards we have known' struck the South. 'Sweeping in from the Straits of Dover, it spread through Bournemouth - where AA patrols said the high winds were 'whipping the snow into a frenzy' - Salisbury and Devizes in little more than fifteen minutes.' Two inches of snow fell 'in little more than an hour' in Hendon and by midnight it was snowing hard from Kent to Somerset.

In Marylebone, 'snowploughs and mechanical diggers will come into action again, and the movement of traffic, let alone the parking of cars, will be gravely impeded by banks of snow and ruts.' In plutocratic Kensington 'they make no use of snowploughs, but shovel the snow away by hand. Some of it follows the route of the Borough's refuse to a wharf in Chelsea, some of it is run down the large sewers of Kensington'. As if drivers did not face enough problems it was reported that stockpiles of salt for gritting roads were running out. Westminster alone had already used 1,100 tons, and Wandsworth had used its entire 700 ton stock and been told that fresh supplies would not arrive for three or four days. Westminster had been given the same response with the added proviso 'weather permitting'.

At the Winsford salt mine in Cheshire, source of virtually all the domestic output of salt for roads, lorries were queuing for two hours before being loaded. British Railways, 'acknowledging that their transport of salt is not at the moment imbued with any sense of urgency, can point out that their entire service is slowed down by the snow which has created the demand for salt'. ICI, owner of the Winsford mine and the chief supplier of road salt, claimed to have done all it could to make supplies available. 'It is chiefly through their persuasive advertising that councils got maximum stocks of salt at "lowest summer prices" months ago.'

To add to the misery, it was reported that meetings of power workers at Barking and Tilbury had voted to join the unofficial work-to-rule and overtime ban already being operated at twelve other London power stations. Power-cuts meant that the supply of car bodies from the Pressed Steel Company's Swindon plant was reduced 'to a trickle' and production of the Morris 100 at Cowley, Oxford, stopped at lunchtime. Production of the A60 at the Austin factory in Birmingham 'resumed again this morning, but stopped at lunchtime' and 500 workers were laid off.

The next day, Thursday 3 January, the work-to-rule led to further power-cuts in London and Essex and part of Barking power station had to be closed altogether. Supplies in Streatham, Hindhead, Hadley in Surrey and Liphook in Hampshire were also cut. Fifteen hours of negotiations between the unions and the Electricity Council over the pay claim for the 128,000 manual workers in the industry broke down without agreement that night. The Electricity Council's increased offer of twopence-halfpenny an hour (one new penny), just over a halfpenny more than their previous offer, was rejected by the unions.

There was more depressing news for householders with the announcement that 'the milk situation' was 'threatening to be desperate' as emergency arrangements for transporting milk from the South-West to London had, like the power workers' negotiations, 'broken down'. Supplies of vegetables were 'very short' and wholesale potato prices on the London markets

Blizzards and icy roads made many city roads impassable.

had risen to '£24-£28 a ton for whites and £25 - £32 for King Edwards'. In addition, the 'condition of some loaded from field clamps is reputed to be far from good'. Agriculture Minister Nicholas Soames chose that moment to announce that if Britain joined the European Common Market, 'some upward adjustments' in food prices were inevitable. The British Sugar Corporation estimated that ten per cent of the previous year's sugar beet crop of 500,000 tons had still not been lifted from the ground and 'would soon be a write-off. Where there has been much frost [ie everywhere] the condition of the beets is still doubtful and some may well already be too far gone to process.'

If the fate of the sugar beet crop did not disturb too many suburban slumbers, the 'thousands of dustbins overflowing' because the refuse collectors had been unable to get through, were becoming a serious problem. In 'hilly Hampstead' the council was collecting fifty less tons of refuse a day than normal. Wandsworth, concentrating on trade waste, distributed paper sacks... which snow and slush immediately rendered useless.

'Snow and sheet ice' had now combined to keep the South-West of England and South Wales paralysed. There was 'heavy snow' in Swansea and blizzards blowing across Devon cut off many more villages there, and grounded helicopters from RAF Chivenor and RAF Culdrose in Cornwall. The AA reported that 'conditions in many areas are as bad, if not worse, than at any time since the snow onslaught began a week ago'.

Snowdrifts burying the face of a building meet the icicles hanging from the roof.

All roads in and out of Bristol were blocked, 4,000 workers at Morris Motors in Cowley, Oxford, were sent home early, partly because of a shortage of components and partly to help them reach their homes before nightfall, and more than a thousand workers were unable to reach the Atomic Research Centre at Harwell. United States airmen had to take to the fields in heavy vehicles to take supplies to the villages of Leckhampstead and Chaddleworth in Berkshire. In the North, all the trans-Pennine roads were impassable because of drifts. In Monmouthshire a retired haulage contractor, Wilfred Benfield, 59, 'had only just taken up his shovel' to help a neighbour clear snow when he collapsed and died. A steelworker, Edward Glyndwr Davies, 54, was found dead, lying face-downwards in the snow in the Goytre Valley in Port Talbot, and Peter Henretty, 50, a lorry driver of Edinburgh collapsed and died as he exchanged names and addresses after 'a minor accident' on a snowbound section of the Great North Road near Berwick'. The Fire Protection Agency warned of the dangers of an increased death toll because 'unthinking householders' were using used 'blow-lamps, lighted candles and a variety of oil heaters to thaw out frozen pipes, often with disastrous results.'

There was a startling variety of weather across the country, with just one thing in common - all of it was bad. As well as the continuing blizzards in the West, there was fog in Kent, and widespread snow and 'icy rain' in the North, while Gatwick Airport was brought to a halt by freezing snow and slush, causing cancellations and overnight delays of flights to France, Germany, Switzerland and the Channel Islands.

There was a slight thaw in the South on 6 January but that only brought fresh problems as the AA warned that roads were 'already cracked or potholed' by the frost and snow, with

Milk deliveries froze solid on the doorstep, with the bottle-top pushed up an inch or more on a column of frozen milk.

some potholes 'over six inches deep. This can easily happen after a prolonged spell of frost or snow and motorists should be on their guard.' Despite the brief warming, the AA added that 'snow- and ice-belts' gripped the South-West, and the South Coast from Devon to Hampshire and northwards to Oxfordshire and Gloucestershire. Almost the whole of Wales, Shropshire and Staffordshire was also snowbound and everywhere 'east of a line from Scotch Corner in Yorkshire to Gairloch in North-West Scotland'. Only Cheshire and Lincolnshire were reported by the AA to be free of the 'Alpine weather conditions.' One of the most notorious winter black spots, the A68 around Carter Bar, was now blocked for twelve miles. An avalanche of hundreds of tons of rock and snow was blocking almost a quarter of a mile of the mainline between Edinburgh and Carlisle near Galashiels, and foghorns had to be used to warn shipping of danger after further blizzards reduced visibility at Flamborough Head in Yorkshire to nil.

There was better news for some trapped by the snow. A shepherd, J Smith, and his wife snowbound for sixteen days at the top of the Lammermuir Hills in Scotland had been reached with supplies, and holidaymakers at the Forest Inn at Hexworthy on Dartmoor - snowbound there since Christmas Day - were finally rescued by the driver of a Land Rover who 'broke through to them'. A Lakeland terrier trapped for sixty hours at Hardcastle Crags near Hebden Bridge scrambled free just as rescuers were giving up for the night. It leapt into the arms of its owner, David Dalgliesh, 'the head keeper on Lord Savile's 16,000 acre estate, and was taken home for its first meal in three days'. There was more good news for animal lovers when police reported that 1,500 stranded sheep, cattle and ponies on Dartmoor had now been rescued and foddered. The rescuers had encountered drifts between twenty and thirty feet deep, and many thousands more animals were still buried under the snow. And a disconsolate Secretary of the National Mouse Club, Percy Ashley, reported that the freezing temperatures had led to 'a sharp fall in the birth rate among Britain's prize mice'. Mr Ashley warned that 'Entries in the baby mice classes at the big January shows will be hit.'

More snow fell on 7 January, heaviest over Scotland, and road conditions everywhere were described by the AA's hyperbolic spokesman as 'satanical'. A farmer at Edmundbyers in County Durham said the snow was 'the worst I have seen. Some of the drifts are as high as houses'. Diesel froze in buses and lorries at Grantown-on-Spey in Morayshire, where the temperature fell to -21C, and railway workers were using dynamite in an attempt to clear the blocked railway line at Riccarton between Carlisle and Edinburgh. On Dartmoor sheep buried by snowdrifts were being 'eaten alive by hungry foxes which are burrowing through the snow to get to them' and police in the New Forest area issued a warning that 'hunger-crazed ponies' might attack people carrying food. A hotel worker, Mrs Linda Parker, had already been 'set upon by two black mares in foal'. As she walked home to her caravan near

Brocklehurst, the ponies 'ran up behind her, bit her and kicked her. She was rescued by two men who chased off the ponies with sticks.' A corporation workman got some revenge against the animal kingdom for such indignities while unloading snow from a lorry parked on a slipway near Margate in Kent. He dropped his shovel into the water and as he bent down to pick it up he saw 'a ten pound cod, measuring two foot six inches' in the water. 'I scooped up my shovel quickly and the cod came with it. It was alive and kicking until I hit it with the shovel'.

Over the next few days the vicious cold continued. There were fresh snowfalls in the North and Scotland on 11 January and by the next day "ice-floes" were forming in the River Thames at Windsor. A bystander saw 'a solitary skiff being rowed along the river, noisily hitting the chunks of ice'. The Thames was soon frozen right across. 'For the first time in memory', the River Arun, 'the second fastest-flowing river in Britain', was frozen over completely where it met the sea at Littlehampton in Sussex. People skated on the ice, fourteen inches thick, that covered the River Avon at Tewkesbury, and at Newnham-on-Severn, three men 'lashed themselves together and walked across the river's icy surface'. Many other lakes and rivers froze, ice covered harbours, the sea froze for some distance from the Kent shore and there were ice-floes and pack-ice off the coasts. Huge blocks of ice were formed on beaches as the spray from breaking waves froze as it landed, and at Torquay and Herne Bay in Kent, 'sea water froze for the first time in living memory, as it crashed over 100 yards of promenade'. The fountains in Trafalgar Square in London were also frozen solid and the pigeons picked their way across the sheet ice surrounding them.

The misery of the bitter cold was compounded by the continuation of the work-to-rule by power station workers. While union officials continued to debate whether to make the dispute official, leaders of the unofficial action called for 'a more rigid application' of the existing work-to-rule. There were voltage reductions at each peak period from 'the Wash to the Sussex Coast'. Fires and lights were dimmer and signalling and switching on Southern Region railway lines was also affected. A surgeon, Frank Musgrove, declared Britain was 'like a jungle' after having to work by candlelight to save a mother whose baby died during a power-cut at Wanstead Hospital, Essex. Priority in the distribution of coal was given to steam trains carrying supplies of food, coal, oil and petrol. As the power workers' action escalated still further, electricity cuts darkened streets, switched off traffic lights, closed cinemas and theatres, and left many other businesses operating by candlelight. Old paraffin heaters were pressed back into service and many fires were caused through heaters being knocked over, or left unattended, often in lofts, in an effort to defrost frozen pipes. Many drivers left a small paraffin heater burning all night under the engine block of their car when they had parked it in their garage. Although such heaters were normally fitted with a safety gauze, it was a miracle that the lethal combination of a naked flame and vapour from petrol engines did not produce more fires and explosions.

Water pipes and mains burst in the cold. It was reported that 200,000 gallons of water a day were being lost to leaks and bursts in the Windsor area alone, and tarpaulins filled with insulation material were hung from Windsor Bridge in an attempt to protect the water-main running along the underside of the bridge, and Brighton Corporation wrapped emergency standpipes in sheets of polythene, 'Inside [of which] is a red lamp to prevent the standpipe from freezing.' The Windsor Express reported that two children aged five and six had turned up clutching 'ready-pasted' toothbrushes at their dentist's surgery, asking if they could clean

Workers digging through a twelve foot drift to free a stranded lorry laden with cattle feed.

their teeth there as the pipes at home were frozen. Pipes freezing and then bursting as they thawed also let thousands of children have days off school and gave plumbers one of their biggest bonanzas in years. As further proof of the truth of the old adage about ill winds, a trader gleefully reported a 'fantastic demand' for buckets.

On 16 January snow returned to the UK with significant falls continuing over several hours in most parts of the country apart from the South-West, which was probably due a reprieve. There was a further very harsh frost that night - the AA described Britain as 'a vast ice patch' - and in London the temperature had now not risen above 3°C for the twenty-five consecutive days since the cold spell began on 23 December. It was another new milestone of misery, the longest comparable spell in the past had been twenty-four days in 1890 and 1895.

Bus passengers in Swansea circulated a petition urging the installation of heaters on the buses, but not all passengers signed it; 'some said they could not sign as their hands were too cold to hold the pen.' There was a different cause of "bus rage" in Doncaster, where a fourteen year-old schoolboy, James Boyle, was turfed off a bus and left to walk eight miles home through thick snow because he'd lost his bus-fare. When he told the conductor, she said, 'Well, you'll have to get off then, won't you?' But 100 yards down the road he was allowed to reboard the bus, after one of the other passengers paid his fare for him. When asked why the boy could not simply have given his name and address to the conductor, the

28 February 1963: Teams of men clearing the snow from Cheltenham racecourse in preparation for the National Hunt Festival beginning on 12 March 1963. The entire course had to be cleared of snow by hand, since machines would have damaged the turf.

Yorkshire Traction Company's spokesman, Mr C Dean, replied, 'If I walk into a shop and find I have no money, I don't leave my name and address. It may cause hardship, but unless there is someone willing to pay the fare, that is the way it is.'

Water and gas mains were again affected by the frost and there was a tragedy in Salford, Lancashire, when five people died of gas poisoning after a four-inch gas main fractured only seven or eight feet from the victims' house. The sole survivor, Ann Hardy, who was just eleven years old, lost her parents, her grandmother and her two brothers. Two days after the incident, doctors had still not broken the news to her that she was now an orphan. She was said to be 'a little better' but doctors advised that she should not be told 'until she is well again, when a priest may be asked to break the news'. Another awful tragedy was averted by inches, thanks to the quick reactions of a lorry driver. Arthur Baxter braked his eleven-ton oil tanker to an emergency stop at Caenby Corner roundabout near Lincoln, when 'two bundles' fell from the car in front of him as it took the roundabout. He got out and found two brothers aged nine and eleven lying in the road. 'My stomach turned over,' he said, 'when I saw the children only about two inches from my wheels. They were screaming and so was a lady in the car'. They survived, having suffered only 'bruising and shaking'.

A tragedy of a somewhat less serious nature was brewing in Doncaster, where a 'women's

The bananas must get through... With no gritters on the streets, drivers had to take matters into their own hands. This lorry driver has wheelbarrowed some grit from a nearby stockpile to try and get his lorry up a snow-covered hill.

underwear crisis' was giving the town's female inhabitants some anxious moments. The manageress of a women's outfitters reported a dearth of warm underwear saying 'I have had to turn away dozens of orders. The makers say they have been taken unawares by the severity of the weather.' But 'London hosiery manufacturers who put on their "Beatniks" - knee-length, woolly bloomers - as a gimmick and found it an all-time winner' were besieged with orders. A spokesman for the company made the curious statement that 'Girls bought the garments for a laugh at first, but find in the cold weather that they can't get out of them.' Meanwhile a looming crisis over the untidy gardens of council homes at Norton, near Malton, was averted when council officials, recognising the impossibility of gardening in sub-zero temperatures gave tenants an extra month to put their unruly gardens in order.

There was an echo of 1947 on 19 January, when, just as in that year, newspapers published a picture of a farmer (this time at Waldringfield in Suffolk), using a pneumatic drill to harvest his carrots and parsnips from his rock-hard frozen fields. 'A production rate of a ton a day is claimed, but some of the carrots are damaged.' They had to be broken out of the clods of earth with a hammer.

That day there were further two-hour power-cuts in London. Traffic lights failed in the West End and extra police were called in to deal with the resulting traffic chaos. AA emergency staff dealing with breakdown calls had to work by candlelight. West End cinemas were blacked out, films stopping in mid-screening and the start of the Kurt Weill Opera at Sadler's Wells was delayed by forty-five minutes until the power came back on.

The temperatures remained bitterly low and the easterly gales, feeling as if they had blown all the way from Siberia, made the situation even worse. Salting the roads was becoming ineffective - the temperatures were so low that even salt water froze. One of the heaters from London Airport had to be installed at the Corporation Depot in Alma Road, Windsor, because the piles of rock salt were frozen into boulders that were impossible to load and use on the gritting lorries. The Western Region of British Rail cancelled several trains because of icing in the savage frost. Steam and diesel locomotives were 'running with difficulty' and 'some were even freezing up while running'.

The vicious easterly gales brought fresh blizzards with them and 'Britain was almost cut in half' with every cross-border road between England and Scotland blocked. More than 200 vehicles were stranded on the A66 at Stainmore - like Carter Bar, a notorious winter black spot - after 'the worst blizzard in sixteen years'. Some drivers abandoned their cars and fought their way through the drifts 'to spend the night at a moorland cafe'. Forty-eight soldiers missing after a twenty-four hour exercise on Dartmoor were found in an empty cottage south of Princetown. All were suffering from frostbite. Their boots had frozen solid when they took them off to bivouac at night and, unable to put them back on again, they walked 'in stockinged feet' 200 yards to the cottage where they were found by a search party. Police patrol cars were sent to search for the Archbishop of Canterbury after he was reported 'very late'. He arrived safely at Canterbury at 10pm after a six hour journey from Lambeth Palace, most of which time had been spent in 'a huge traffic jam near Swanley'. On the railways, gangs of men battled for hours to dig out an Edinburgh to London express that was completely covered by a snowdrift 'on a wild Pennine moor' near Dent in North Yorkshire. The railwaymen eventually managed to release the rear three coaches and the fifty-seven passengers were taken the sixty miles back to Carlisle and 'given refreshments' before continuing their journey via Newcastle. 100 railwaymen were meanwhile continuing to try and free the locomotive and the first five coaches of the snowbound train. Other lines in the area were blocked by fallen trees brought down by gales.

The following day, in 'one of the biggest airlifts ever, four jet-powered helicopters' evacuated 283 staff from the Fylingdales Early Warning Station on the North Yorkshire Moors, who had been trapped there for five days with fuel supplies running low. 'Almost every piece of snow-clearing equipment had been lost' in an attempt to force a way through twelve-foot drifts and Max Goldman, the American site manager of the euphemistically named Radio Corporation of America at Fylingdales, said that weather conditions were 'unbelievable', worse than anything he had experienced during the construction of an early warning station in Alaska. 'The wind is blowing at between seventy and eight miles an hour,' he said, 'and no one is allowed to go outside alone. It is too dangerous out there.' The snow was being driven so hard by the gale that it covered a double-decker bus in less than an hour. Despite the gales, the staff were ferried out in batches of eight to ten, and taken to Whitby twelve miles away. 111 civilian workers were still stranded at Fylingdales when flights were suspended at nightfall, and they were forced to endure another night trapped on the moors.

The gales and snow sweeping the country created chaos everywhere. Despite the police putting 'every available man on point duty' there was a fifteen mile traffic-jam in Halifax, as

Bad news for parents, good news for kids - Scottish schoolchildren making good use of a fresh snowfall.

thousands of vehicles made for the only road still open into Lancashire, and at one stage it was taking five hours to cover the eleven miles from Halifax to Todmorden. Workmen gave up any hope of opening any of the other trans-Pennine roads; 'as fast as a stretch of road is cleared, it fills in again as the snow is whipped up by the strong winds.' On the worst stretches of road, drifts of thirty and forty feet deep were reported. On the Settle-Carlisle line, railwaymen worked all day for the second day running in an unavailing attempt to free the locomotive and five coaches trapped at Dent. Flights were halted yet again at London Airport after an Austrian airliner hit a patch of 'glazed ice' and skidded off the runway. BEA had to cancel forty-four flights and divert a dozen others. The AA said that roads in eighty of the eighty-six English, Welsh and Scottish counties were now impassable because of snow or abandoned vehicles. British Rail's Western Region announced that it was cancelling twenty-three services a day 'until the weather improves' and there were heavy delays on the Southern Region because of snow, freezing rain and icing of rails and points. The 10.10am from Ramsgate did not reach Victoria until 5.20pm.

Two men were missing after their tug capsized in the icy waters of the River Humber. The sixty-five year-old skipper of the tug, Mr H Ellerby, and the engineer, thirty year-old Benjamin Leary, were both missing believed drowned, but the skipper's twenty year-old son who managed to swim 200 yards to the shore and 'struggled, exhausted through frozen mud to

A not very sun-blessed Morris 1000 in the winter of 1962-63

reach a cottage', was recovering in hospital. The twenty-two man crew of the Lebanese cargo ship *Alfotis* were rescued after running aground on the Herd Sands at the mouth of the Tyne. But rescuers failed to reach the infelicitously named *Sunk* lightship off Harwich, where a lamplighter, R Buckland, had broken his ribs in a fall; for the first time in forty years lifeboatmen at Walton couldn't board their boat moored to the pier. A sixty year-old North Sea Pilot, Commander Albert Longmuir of Petworth in Sussex drowned off Dungeness after he fell into the sea while boarding the American ship *Blue Jacket*.

Police searching an area around an abandoned car at Belthorn near Blackburn found the body of John Yates, 48, the father-in-law of the Manchester City and England inside-forward Peter Dobing, but in the Lake District, a twenty-man rescue team working by floodlights and using ladders, ropes and a boat, rescued Mr and Mrs Curwen of Belle Isle, Bowness-on-Windermere, after 'a three hour ordeal'. They had fallen through the ice while crossing the frozen lake to their home. Ten Glasgow families also had a narrow escape when the end wall of a four-storey tenement in Barloch Street Glasgow collapsed in the gales. All of them managed to scramble to safety.

Two twenty year-old students were rescued after being buried by an avalanche between Rochdale and Edenfield but, despite a five hour search by a team of more than twenty people, the third member of their party was still missing at nightfall when the search was suspended. It would resume at daybreak but hopes of his survival were slim. Police and rescue teams also carried out a day-long search for two climbers buried under a 100-ton avalanche at Chew Valley, Saddleworth. Both men, Graham West, 29, of Stalybridge, and Michael Roberts, 27, of Dukinfield, were married and members of the Manchester Gritstone Climbing Club. The search was abandoned at midnight when no trace of them had been found. Their bodies, and that of the missing student, David Leith, 20, buried by an avalanche, were found the next day.

That day, 21 January, the last 111 civilian workers were flown out of Fylingdales by helicopter, but rescue came too late for sixty-two year-old William Bailey who was found dead on his farm at Allerton in Bradford, buried in a snowdrift. Ambulance men had to battle through waist-high snow to reach the farm and help dig out the body. Four elderly women also died in three separate incidents after the frost caused gas mains to fracture. Mrs Rhoda Thompson from Bradford, Mrs Ivy Cousins and Mrs Winifred McKeenan, widows who lived in neighbouring cottages in Seaton, Devon, and Mrs Harriet Kite of Bath were all poisoned by leaking gas. A gas-boiler explosion also injured four people at Garston near Watford. Plumber Leslie Wyatt who was working on the boiler at the time, suffered head injuries when the blast 'threw him from the kitchen along the hall to the front door'.

As the frost bit ever deeper, the Humber was frozen in places four inches thick and 'the wakes of the ships froze before they could disperse'. Southend pier was surrounded by sheet and pack ice, which stretched for more than a mile into the Thames estuary. A further attempt to take the injured man off the *Sunk* lightship off Harwich failed again because of continuing bad weather.

In Westmorland, the springs that normally supplied cattle herds with water had been frozen solid for eight days and reserve supplies were running out. Kendal firemen had to deliver 400 gallons to Ellenwray Farm at Old Hutton when 'forty Ayrshire cows had nothing to drink'. Human problems were eased by British Rail which, with Peak District roads 'blocked by nearly twenty-foot drifts, with cars, vans and buses abandoned', agreed to reopen the Buxton to Ashbourne line, closed to passenger traffic for more than a year. Preceded by a snowplough, a special train pulled by two engines set out for Buxton, laden with bread, milk and other supplies.

Power-cuts were again occurring and police escorted a mobile generator borrowed from a building site in Stoke Newington to the Garrett Anderson Maternity Home in Hampstead, where 'the incubators sustaining three babies' had been affected by power-cuts that blacked out Hampstead. At Hampstead General, where another three babies were in incubators, staff asked police for a battery 'to keep the oxygen supply going'.

On 23 January the temperature dropped still further and the coldest night of the winter left thousands of diesel vehicles stranded. 200 London buses froze up on the roads, mainly in Hounslow and Barnet, and the AA reported that lorry drivers on the Barnet by-pass were 'lighting small fires under their lorries to thaw out their frozen fuel systems'. Over a hundred vehicles were abandoned on the M1, twenty more on 'a road leading in at the Birmingham end', and mist and fog made the roads even more hazardous - 'the worst driving conditions of the winter', according to the RAC, leading to a twenty-seven car pile-up in fog near Toddington. London Airport was fogbound and a Whirlwind helicopter from Manston in Kent had to airlift heating fuel to a ship frozen into the ice at the mouth of the Blackwater River in Essex. The death toll from the cold continued, with the body of a seventy-two year-old Aberavon woman found frozen in the snow, just a handful of yards from her front door.

By 24 January there were the first hopeful signs since the cold snap began, with weather forecasters predicting a slight thaw and a modest improvement in coal and power supplies. The National Coal Board said that fourteen trains had been loaded at East Midlands pits to take coal to 'points where merchants could collect it', and 1,500 lorries took part in 'an emergency coal lift' to power stations and homes. Although the Wales Gas Board had 'stopped selling appliances as an emergency measure', restrictions on Welsh gas supplies were also eased, but elsewhere there was more bleak news. 2,200 of Oldham's 2,600 gas-lamps were out of action and most of the remaining lights were 'giving little more than a glimmer'. Freezing fog in the West Midlands dislocated electricity supplies when thick ice formed on power lines, there were more power-cuts in Kent and water rationing in Carmarthenshire because the mountain streams that normally fed the reservoirs were all frozen solid. As a result, water was cut off from 9.30pm to 5.30am every night. Already dangerously low, supplies were further threatened when a main burst in Carmarthen, leaving half the town without water for another fourteen hours.

The football pools companies had been losing money hand over fist since the cold snap began and after three successive pools coupons had been wiped out by postponements caused by the weather, they took steps to reduce their losses. For the first time ever, a "Pool's Panel" was set-up with "The Five Just Men" - retired footballers Ted Drake, Tom Finney, Tommy Lawton and George Young, and retired referee Arthur Ellis - were recruited to predict the results of games that had been postponed because of snow and ice. The panel, paid £100 each for their trouble and meeting under the chairmanship of Lord Brabazon, sat for the first time on the following Saturday, 26 January 1963.

The state of the weather suggested that the Pools Panel would be meeting regularly over the next few weeks, and there was unlikely to have been much popular sympathy for the proprietors of "England's longest ski run" at Edale in Derbyshire, who, alone among their fellow-countrymen, were complaining of a shortage of snow. They explained that strong winds during the week had blown away most of the snow on the ski-run. Elsewhere there was more than enough snow and ice for everyone. Hardraw Force, at 100 feet the highest single-drop waterfall in England, was almost completely frozen. There was 'a solid block of ice' seventy feet wide and fifty feet high at the foot of the waterfall and one of the 'giant icicles' hanging from the upper edge was sixty feet long. A cat was found frozen by its tail to the corrugated iron roof of an outbuilding in York, and frost cracked a plate-glass display inside a confectioner's shop and 'sent jars of sweets crashing down'.

'Thousands of huge ice-floes, many of them more than thirty feet across' were carried up the River Taw in Devon by the high tide. They piled up against the two bridges at Barnstaple and 'soon there was a solid mass of packed ice, many feet thick, extending right across the 500-foot wide river.' On Merseyside where the daytime temperature was -11°C, two of the three docks at Garston were frozen up and in Yorkshire, the Humber Conservancy Board warned that it was 'extremely hazardous to attempt navigation of the icebound river'. All the channel marker buoys between the River Trent and Hull had been cast adrift or dragged off-station by the ice-packs that stretched from Goole to the North Sea, a distance of forty-seven miles.

Fourteen girls aged between fifteen and seventeen were taken to hospital after being 'overcome by cold while travelling in a coach from Basildon to London' and the British Medical Journal carried a warning to mothers about the dangers of hypothermia to babies. Mothers were instructed to 'feel the baby's face and extremities from time to time in cold weather'. Almost the only people feeling the heat were the fifty families evacuated from a building in Streatham after a fault in the central heating system caused 'radiators and pipes to buckle with the intense heat'. The families stood shivering in the courtyard for an hour while firemen worked to "draw out" the fire in the boiler. 'The whole building was shaking and the noise was terrifying.'

Wildlife was badly affected by the cold. Mrs Joan Sydenham, 40, was staying alone on the icebound Long Island in Poole Harbour, trying to save thousands of starving seabirds

Only the marker posts and telegraph poles show where the snowbound moors end and the road begins.

sheltering there. Foxes were raiding dustbins and 'decimating' the Chipping Norton cats and a man driving a bulldozer on the Burford road in the Cotswolds was 'picking up dead pigeons and small birds for three days or so'. For several miles along the Tewkesbury road out of Stow-on-the-Wold, skeletal rabbits and hares could be seen 'running about on the verges, ignoring the sound of the car. They are nothing but skin and bone and I suppose come down to the road to eat the bark of the trees'. In a scene that could have come from Hitchcock's film *The Birds* - released that year - a woman carrying bread rolls on the top of her shopping basket was attacked by hundreds of starving pigeons as she walked across Town Hall Square in Leicester. 'As they tore at the rolls, she was knocked off her feet. She then got up and ran off.'

The appalling weather was not confined to Britain, with a savage winter right across the Northern Hemisphere. Only in parts of Scandinavia and some parts of the far North was the temperature milder than usual, with Western Norway recording a January temperature of 6°C. There were blizzards in Japan, where twenty people died in an avalanche, and in the USA, the temperature in Jackson, Mississippi, fell 12°C in a single hour, Bowling Green, Kentucky recorded a low of -29°C and Atlanta -19°C, the coldest temperature there since 1899. Further north, a fifteen-foot thick ice-floe blocked the mouth of the Niagara River, while tons of ice tumbling over the Niagara Falls formed mounds 'up to seventy feet high' in the lower river.

In Europe, 230 villages were cut off by snow in the Apennines, there was ten inches of snow in Bari, right down in the "heel" of Italy, and tourists seeking a little winter sunshine in the Sicilian town of Taormina were 'throwing snowballs at each other'. It even snowed in

Telegraph wires are bowed to breaking point by the weight of ice and a railway water tank is smothered in icicles.

Tunisia. In Belgrade and Bavaria the temperature dropped below -32°C, and Swiss lakes and rivers were frozen, some for the first time since 1929. However, unlike London Airport, Zurich's Kloten Airport remained open every day throughout the long cold spell. An airport employee had devised a mixture containing alcohol and 'a secret ingredient' as an antifreeze for his car, but having tested it as an aircraft and runway de-icer, it was pressed into service at the airport. 'All the trials having been successful, the Zurich Airport had a motor tank constructed holding 1,350 gallons with twenty-four-foot hoses on either side for spraying the runways. It takes from thirty-five to forty minutes to spray the main runway and the ice melts within five to fifteen minutes.' Each application cost £100 but the airport found the process 'highly profitable, as seventy aircraft landed and paid £1600 in airport duties'.

In Denmark a cinema owner from Randers took bread rather than money as the price of admission, so that he could feed the starving wild birds, and French firemen had to rescue seagulls after their feet froze onto the ice on the River Rhone and in Germany the upper Rhine froze for the first time in thirty-four years and barges were at a standstill in Bonn. The ice blocking the river greatly reduced its flow, causing problems downstream when sea water penetrated further upstream than usual and penetrated the Maas, a Dutch tributary of the Rhine from which Rotterdam drew much of its water supply. The city's water became 'undrinkable' with a salt water content ten times the normal level, and Rotterdam grocers began selling fresh water at 3d (just over one new penny) per litre.

On 24 and 25 January the promised slight thaw made a brief appearance in northern England and Scotland. The temperature in Bridlington jumped 12°C in three hours, but the thaw triggered avalanches on the Snake Pass between Sheffield and Manchester. After blasting operations failed to clear the snow and rock debris, it was announced that the pass would remain closed for another fourteen days. The thaw also caused 100 bursts in the water mains in Ribbleton, near Preston in Lancashire, and turned many miles of roads into 'rivers of slush'. In the South the temperature remained well below zero. At Gatwick it fell to -13°C and freezing fog caused power-cuts in London and Brighton. There were also power-cuts in Derbyshire, where five ice-cream vans used their generators to provide warmth and light for premature babies at two Derby hospitals. Luton endured an eighteen-hour power-cut after cables and condensers became frozen, and water supplies in Mid-Bedfordshire 'failed totally'. In the hope of saving water, with supplies now 'drying up all over the country', women were urged to 'forget washday' and keep their dirty clothes until the weather improved. There was a faint hope of an improvement in the power supply situation with the news that eighty shiploads of coal left the North-East for London, the South and the South-West, while 4,000 lorries were 'working through the weekend' in a 'blitzkrieg-style operation' to move coal.

Army engineers used dynamite to break up ice on the River Colne in Essex so that four ships at Hythe Quay could put to sea, and there were reports of hundreds of 'frozen suppers' washing ashore there and all along the East Coast, as conger eels 'killed by the big freeze-up' were washed ashore. Experts said that it was forty-six years - the terrible winter of 1917 - since the waters of the North Sea had last been cold enough to kill the eels. A Boulogne fishmonger's clerk would have had some sympathy for the eels. The newspapers reported that he had moved his desk to the cold storage room among the fish because it was warmer than the office. 'It's 2°C in there [the cold storage room]' he said, 'and the temperature is -6°C in my office.'

While a few eels may have been a welcome addition to some families' diet, attempts to improve the supply of other food were hampered not just by the weather but by the depredations of starving wildlife. Market gardeners were 'waging a shooting war' against starving pigeons eating spring broccoli and 100 head of deer from Scrivelsby Court Park, Horncastle, 'home of the Queen's Champion, Major J Dymoke, were invading neighbouring farmland and eating kale and root crops intended for sheep'.

A moderate improvement in the weather that weekend appeared to have come too late for an escapee from Dartmoor prison, Robert Crook, 34, who had absconded from a working party with another man, but was now feared dead, after police searching the edge of a plantation two miles from the prison on the Tavistock to Exeter road, found erratic 'footprints and marks in the snow, suggesting the journey of an exhausted man'. His fellow-prisoner had been recaptured unharmed.

The slow thaw strengthened that weekend but that brought fresh problems in its wake. Rail tunnels from the South-West to Kent were closed because of the danger from falling ice. The Metropolitan Water Board reported that it was 'inundated with reports of burst pipes'. Hundreds of rare books were damaged when a pipe burst in the old library of Trinity College, Oxford, and when a water main burst in Southampton Row in London, water 'swept like a wave down the street. Jets forced up paving stones and thousands of gallons poured into the site of the New Bedford Hotel'. Twenty-four hours later, firemen were still pumping out flooded basements of shops and hotels, and parts of Southampton Row remained closed for a further week. Large ice-floes - some 'four feet thick and half an acre in extent' - broke away from the frozen Langstone Harbour near Portland and tore away the anchors and cables of more than a dozen yachts and cabin cruisers, setting them adrift.

Insurance companies added to the general air of gloom by announcing that they were facing tens of thousands of claims totalling an estimated £15 million, 'the most expensive winter ever'. Farmers in East Anglia had their own financial woes to worry about, as the British Sugar Corporation reported that sugar beet still frozen in the ground was now 'likely to be unsuitable for sugar manufacture'. Farmers could not even use the spoiled crop as fodder for their animals as 'it may be dangerous... we recommend that expert advice should be obtained before doing so.'

The month of January had been one of the most miserable in British history - the coldest month of the entire twentieth century. Mean minimum temperatures were well below freezing almost everywhere in England, Wales and Scotland, and even the mean maximum temperatures were at or below freezing in many areas. Between 23 December 1962 and 25 January, 1963, the weather station at Moor House in Westmorland - a relatively low-lying station - recorded thirty-four consecutive days with a maximum temperature of zero°C or below. At higher altitudes, the temperatures were markedly colder, with Braemar recording a low of -22.2°C on 18 January. There were air frosts throughout southern England and South Wales on 25 of the 31 nights during the month, and even at normally mild Kew, the temperature never rose above 2.7°C at any time in the whole month. The CET (Central England Temperature) has, since 1659, recorded the monthly average temperatures for an area roughly bounded by Preston, Bristol and London, and in January 1963, the CET of -2.1°C, was 4-5°C below normal, and even lower than the -1.9°C recorded in February 1947.

The weather had helped to drive up unemployment, which 'reached new peaks' in January, while industrial production had fallen nine per cent below the November level. The one modest consolation amongst this catalogue of woe was that between the blizzards, the high pressure and clear skies that characterised the savage frosts made for sunny days. Weather stations in the West, from the Hebrides, through Prestwick, Manchester and Aberporth to Chivenor, recorded twice the normal monthly average of sunshine hours.

The change in month brought no let-up in the weather, with the return of fog and snow marked by falls of two inches in Essex. The emergency 'coal-lift' to the South continued with around one hundred 'trimmers and teemers' in Sunderland working in blinding snowstorms to load 10,000 tons of coal into ships bound for the Thames. In the East Midlands another 4,000 lorries took part in a second 'emergency lift' of 50,000 tons. Most went to power stations and to homes in the London and Bristol areas, but a Bath coal merchant 'recruited 400 lorries' from as far away as Weston-super-Mare and Bristol. 'In 100 years, there has never been so much coal distributed in one day in Bath.'

On 5 February, rubbing the noses of his fellow Britons in their winter misery, Commodore FG Wallis, the new master of the Queen Elizabeth, remarked that the liner's voyage to New York had been 'practically summer cruising', the noon temperature on arrival in New York being 14°C. As he made his remarks, gales and yet another blizzard were sweeping his home country. More than 130,000 miles of roads were affected. There were gusts of seventy-five miles an hour at Ronaldsway, Isle of Man, and sixty-nine miles an hour in Blackpool. Two elderly sisters, Misses Ellen and May Saunders, were found dead of hypothermia in their caravan at West Kingsdom, Kent. The West Country was again almost cut off from the rest of the country, with not a single road open into Cornwall. After 'some of the worst blizzards in the memory of many people in South Wales' eighty men assisted by six snowploughs finally succeeded in digging their way through to an ambulance stuck in the drifts between Aberaeron and Aberystwyth. It was carrying farmer David Williams, 26, of Lampeter, who had

Imprisoned in ice - many canals and rivers froze solid, trapping boats until the spring thaw.

been seriously injured in a tractor accident. Fire Brigade officials advised the Thames Valley Water Board to 'discontinue the method of sending electrical charges through pipes to thaw them'. The warning came after the method caused fires in two houses in Reading. The Water Board refused to discontinue the practice but announced that 'water engineers will be accompanied in future by an electrician and a gas fitter'.

The next day, the editor of *The Times* had had enough of winter and its attendant problems and complained in an irritable editorial that 'some deaths, much misery and general inconvenience are the prize the nation has paid since Christmas for being unready' for the harsh weather. He went on to lambast in turn the water, gas and electricity supply boards, the railways, national and local government and 'last but not least in the catalogue of ineptitude, the strongly entrenched British tradition of jerry-building in plumbing. Cisterns and pipes are installed in our island homes as a sacrifice to the ice gods. Their placing is such that often blockage or burst is a near certainty in a bad winter.'

Whether through the intervention of *The Times* or the ice gods, a thaw set in the next day, bringing the inevitable floods in its wake. Boscastle in Cornwall was flooded when thousands of gallons of meltwater swept debris down the valley and blocked the River Jordan. The thaw continued the next day, 7 February, with the River Exe bursting its banks between Stoke Canon and Exeter. 15,000 sandbags, blankets and radio equipment were being stockpiled in Devon. Troops were on standby and Army engineers used dynamite to break up 'huge ice-floes' on the Rivers Axe and Exe, and to blow up an ice-jam that was backing up flood waters threatening to sweep away the main Exeter to Lyme Regis road. In Wales, a fifty year-old man from Swansea was drowned in the River Amman in Carmarthenshire when he fell while trying to break up an ice-floe on the river.

While the thaw gathered pace in the South-West, Scotland was experiencing its worst snowfalls of the winter. A Wigtown snowplough was 'struggling to take supplies' to six adults and eleven children trapped in a school and adjoining house at Meoul near Portpatrick. An RAF helicopter from RAF Leuchars, 150 miles north-east of the school, had been forced to turn back and another attempt to take food to railwaymen stranded at Riccarton Junction, Roxburghshire also had to be aborted. Of the cross-border routes, only the A1 and the Dumfries to Carlisle roads were still open. Nineteen passengers on the 1.25pm train from Mallaig, Inverness-shire to Glasgow were stuck all night in snowdrifts between Bridge of Orchy, Argyllshire and Tyndrum, Perthshire. They eventually reached Glasgow after nightfall the following day. Passengers on the 4.25pm train were also heavily delayed; among them, appropriately enough, was Colonel Donald Cameron, chairman of the Scottish Railway Board.

In England a bus carrying thirty-five schoolchildren plunged into a dyke and overturned after it collided with a car on an icy road near Sleaford in Lincolnshire. 'The children had to scramble on top of the bus after the crash and jump eight feet into frozen snow to safety'. Miraculously only three children were injured and only one of them hospitalised with a broken arm. A helicopter crashed about ten miles from Darlington shortly after taking off during a snowstorm from the RAF station at Middleton St George. The pilot 'decided the weather was too severe and tried to land in a field, but the helicopter lurched over and cartwheeled for 100 yards on its rotor blades.' Both the pilot and his passenger scrambled out unhurt. An Army helicopter, one of seven carrying out missions to isolated farms in Northern Ireland, also crashed near Mossley, County Antrim, but once more the pilot escaped unharmed.

In response to emergency appeals from all parts of the country, the Red Cross sent out '500 blankets and fifty cartons of soup to Glamorgan for sick old people; coconut mats to Penzance; scrubbing brushes, floor cloths and disinfectant to help in clearing up flooded homes in Montgomeryshire; blankets to Halifax, Yorks; and babies' napkins, blankets, pillowcases, floor cloths, mops and soap to Northern Ireland.' The purpose of the coconut mats was not explained.

The next day the immediate threat of serious flooding in the South-West had eased a little, though ice was still jamming bridges and 'the long-term situation was still critical'. Further north, the Scottish borders were still snowbound with a five-mile queue of vehicles on the A76 from Cumnock to Dumfries 'trying to grope their way south'. Bad weather again prevented an air-drop of supplies to the adults and children trapped in the Wigtownshire school, but reporters from the BBC and three rival newspapers 'tramped across the snow-covered fields, taking bread and tinned meat' to them.

On 9 February, a team of quarrymen employed by Derbyshire County Council made the 700-foot ascent of the mountain overlooking the Snake Pass in the Peak District and used gelignite to blast away a twenty-five foot overhang of snow threatening the road. It was so cold that the eyelashes of some of the men froze shut. After the blast, 'giant bulldozers and a snow-blower then went into action to sweep away the avalanche and the tremendous task' of reopening the pass was finally completed. However, further snow fell continually all the following day, blocking the pass to traffic once more. In Essex the AA reported that the temperature was 'diving', turning roads into 'glittering sheets of ice'. Cars were 'skating' along main roads and traffic on minor roads was virtually halted.

A few days' respite from the worst of the weather followed, but on 15 February winter returned with a vengeance. There were heavy snowfalls from Hampshire, Wiltshire and Dorset in the South, through Derbyshire, Lincolnshire and Yorkshire to the Moray Firth and beyond. Railway lines from Glasgow to Fort William and Edinburgh to Carlisle were blocked, and conditions on the A9 Perth to Inverness road were described as 'the worst of the winter', with cars and lorries completely buried in fifteen-foot drifts near Kingussie. In England, roads in the Peak District and Yorkshire Dales were impassable and in Wales, roads between Brecon and Swansea and Merthyr were blocked. In the North-East, sheep rescued from snowdrifts were found to be 'suffering from snow-blindness', according to Mr EE Milner of the National Farmers' Union. 'They have been taken under cover and are recovering.' Further south, floods were now affecting new areas with waters rising rapidly in the Stour Valley and Blackmore Vale areas of North Dorset and East Somerset, where hundreds of acres were already under water. Children had to be rescued from several schools by farm tractors. As if all this was not enough, MPs found time to berate the Air

An old steam tug, Mayflower, leading the tanker barge Keeldale H through the ice on the Gloucester and Sharpness Canal in January 1963. The ice was so bad that the tug had to be brought out of retirement to help with the job of keeping the canal open.

The tug Primrose hauling the first of a line of ships past the Quedgeley oil terminal on the Canal. Convoys of ships were formed to try and keep the canal open.

A car swept away by floods.

Ministry for its decision to begin giving temperatures in Celsius instead of Fahrenheit; there were complaints about public 'disgust, unhappiness and inability to follow temperatures given by the Air Ministry in Centigrade [Celsius]'.

Whatever system was used, temperatures remained well below freezing in the North, where two men's attempts to provide relief for swans on the frozen River Wharfe in Otley, Yorkshire, only earned the disapproval of the RSPCA. 'Armed with pickaxes and hatchets', they broke holes in the ice-covered river but were told by RSPCA Inspector Albert Drew, 'You are doing more harm than good.' The deaths of two of the sixteen swans on the river had provoked 'irate animal lovers to contact the RSPCA to ask, "What are you doing about it?" They received an equally straightforward reply: "Nothing".' Inspector Drew claimed that 'in all probability the two swans had died because they were attacked by rats' and said that he had paid several visits to Otley during the past few weeks, 'and I don't think there is anything wrong with the swans. They are quite comfortable on the ice and well fed. If people go breaking the ice haphazardly, it will be more likely to freeze over completely because of the small ice-floes, and swans resting in the water could be trapped.'

A far more serious threat to wild birds was highlighted by news of 'an alarming decline' in the numbers of wildbirds in general and birds of prey in particular - the "Silent Spring" about which Rachel Carson had written in her seminal book published in 1962. Concern was fuelled by reports of 'thousands of birds that fell out of the sky in agony' near Caistor in Lincolnshire. An official at Caistor Hospital 'where hundreds of birds fell' reported that, 'These birds were screeching in pain and I killed several myself'. RSPCA officials took some of the dead birds away for a post-mortem but no obvious cause was found. Rachel Carson and many others felt that the most plausible cause for such incidents and the decline of wild birds in general was the number of toxic chemicals, including DDT, being used on the land. However, a Ministry of Agriculture spokesman was at pains to claim that there was 'no cause for alarm, provided chemicals are used discriminately. We have a voluntary agreement with the farmers not to use certain chemicals at certain times of the year.' DDT did not seem to be affecting a million-strong flock of starlings roosting in a nine-acre wood in West Cumberland. 'Gunshots have little effect on the birds and they ignored blasting operations on some nearby rocks. When they are settled in, they make so much noise that it appears that the explosions affect only birds on the fringes of the flock.' At dawn, 'the birds take off together like a mushroom cloud from an atomic bomb and disperse before returning to the desolate wood at nightfall'.

With disruption on the railways now easing, there was an ominous warning that the cuts to the rail network proposed by "the butcher of the railways" Dr Beeching, would be 'more severe than the most pessimistic estimate so far, because lines will be closed by the hundred'. It was hardly the ideal moment for Dr Beeching to show off a new range of uniforms for British Railways staff, albeit long overdue, the first redesign in fifty years. Sydney Greene, General Secretary of the National Union of Railwaymen, gave the redesign his grudging approval, saying 'Railwaymen are the worst-dressed public servants, so anything is an improvement.'

The worst of the winter had now passed and there were no more heavy snowfalls, though temperatures remained very low with harsh night frosts throughout the rest of the month. The snow still lying in the North proved a boon to police who used 'Sherlock Holmes-type detective work' to arrest a thirty-nine year-old labourer who had attacked a teenage girl. He left a trail of 'diamond-patterned heelprints in the snow' that police followed to his front door. Newspaper sub-editors desperate for new slants on the winter weather must have been saying prayers of thanks for the story that broke on 26 February when Maxwell Fletcher, 17, a Dublin cadet officer who had been at sea only two months proved the hero of a fire aboard the British tanker Abadesa in the River Scheldt. Although 'covered in ice', for ninety minutes he remained at his post on the deck of the blazing ship - prompting endless tabloid variants on 'the boy stood on the burning deck' theme - directing the jet of a hose into the fire threatening the ship. Chief Officer T Woolcott of Bournemouth said, 'It was about ninety minutes before he was relieved and by then he was solidly covered in ice, but not complaining. His chest seemed to be a solid block of ice.'

If not quite as cold as January, February had been exceptionally bitter. Snow fell somewhere in the country on twenty of the first twenty-three days of the month, and during the whole of February, County Durham experienced an air frost every single night. Kent and Essex went eleven consecutive days with unbroken frost and, taken together, the three months - December, January and February - constituted 'the coldest winter in the London area since before 1841'.

In the last days of February and the first days of March 1963, sunny weather raised afternoon temperatures to four or five degrees, but the clear skies saw temperatures plummeting again at night, and it was not until 4 March that mild south-westerlies brought rain and rising temperatures. The warmth led to 'Spring fever' on the roads with the RAC estimating that 15,000 vehicles an hour were leaving London for the coast.

On 6 March, the daytime temperature in London reached 17°C - the highest since 25 October of the previous year - and the night that followed was the first frost-free one right across the country. With the thaw came more flooding, but on nothing like the scale of the 1947 floods, and the Thames Conservancy deliberately lowered the water level in the river to break up the remaining ice that, weakened by the thaw, was a serious hazard to children

Floodwaters roaring through the appropriately-named Canal Road in Bradford.

venturing on to it. As if in emphasis of that, twin boys wearing cowboy hats disappeared after falling into the swollen River Wear at Sunderland, a few yards from their home. The body of one of them was retrieved from the river later that day. And an eight year-old boy was missing believed drowned after being swept away by flood waters at Newton Aycliffe, County Durham. Malcolm Walker 'put his foot in the water to see how deep it was and suddenly slipped. Then the current swept him away.' The boy and his brother had been warned by their primary school headmaster earlier that day not to walk home by the beck because of the flooding. Police called off the search for the missing boy at nightfall.

Ice-floes 'as big as dining tables' swept twenty miles down the River Tyne, 'causing chaos among small craft'. On the River Ouse in York, people, 'gathered to watch the ice crash into the moored barges', faced another danger when 'the concrete bordering of the bank, loosened by the frosts', began cracking. And the A66 Penrith-Scotch Corner road was closed at Brough after it collapsed; 'the road sagged and holes began appearing'.

Canoeing enthusiast Clive Baker took time off from his job as Halifax Town coach to paddle his own canoe - on the pitch. Floods covered part of the ground to a depth of two feet and Clive took the opportunity of getting in some useful practice.

As the winter came to an end, government and people began to count the cost in lost income and extraordinary expenditure. Household fuel bills had skyrocketed, many factories had been on short-time working or temporary closure because of power-cuts. Many farms in remote upland regions had been isolated for over two months, tens of thousands of sheep had been lost and crops worth millions of pounds lost or severely damaged. There was a sharp increase in unemployment in the building trades, and a steep rise in insurance premiums. Local authorities also faced a huge bill for road repairs after frost-heave, as well as the short-term costs of keeping the roads clear - five million cubic yards of snow were moved from Gloucestershire roads alone, and the North-West counties estimated their total bill because of the severe weather at in excess of £1 million, and Lancashire County Council alone spent £400,000 keeping the roads clear.

The winter of 1962-63 was over but, if not the longest, or the snowiest - snowfalls were heavier in 1947, and the depths of lying snow even greater - but 'from the point of view of large areas of the country being under snow, this has been the worst winter since 1814'. And 1962-63 was to remain the coldest winter of the twentieth century and the second coldest ever recorded - only 1739-40 has ever been worse.

The two most familiar words in the English language that winter. It was often impossible to tell where a road ended and the fields began.

ROAD CLOSED

PART V

The Winter of Discontent – 1978-79

If 1947 and 1962-63 were snowier and colder respectively, probably no winter in history inflicted more misery on the hapless British population than 'The Winter of Discontent' of 1978-79. The dominant themes of the winter were established early and every subsequent deterioration in the weather seemed to be matched by a worsening chill in the climate of industrial relations.

There had been spells of snow in November and early December, and rainfall in December was three times the normal average in the Midlands, the East and North-East, and London had its 'wettest December since records began', but the real force of winter was not felt until Christmas was approaching. There were sharp frosts in the week before Christmas and on the last day before the holiday, Friday 22 December, the newspapers headlined the threat of a strike by tanker drivers planned for 3 January. 10,000 troops were reported to be on standby to take over delivery of fuel and the RAC issued a condemnation of the panic buying of petrol that was already leading to shortages in some areas. BBC television and radio were blacked out by strikes, electricity and gas price rises of eight per cent were announced and, just to add to the festive cheer, supplies of the traditional accompaniment to the Christmas turkey - sprouts - were in very short supply. The heavy frosts 'which turn sprouts black' had stopped picking on Tuesday and Wednesday of that week and much of the cauliflower and 'open field celery' crops had also suffered frost damage.

It was not a white Christmas in England and Wales, but there were heavy falls of snow and rain in the north of Scotland on 23 December and the snow spread slowly southwards, though at first the only roads badly affected were in the Dundee and Perth areas. However, the Cairngorms already had a good covering from the earlier snows and the fresh falls triggered avalanches that killed two climbers on a Christmas expedition. On Boxing Day, the bodies of Ian Kershaw, 35, of Oldham, and Colin Shaw, 28, of Leeds, were found in a corrie after a day-long search.

The papers the next day reported a speech by the Shadow Chancellor, Geoffrey Howe, in which he described 1978 as 'the year of the bloody-minded', citing the strikes, go-slows and work-to-rules that at various times had blacked out the BBC, ITN and YTV, stopped trains running on Wednesdays, dried up the petrol pumps, brought the criminal justice system to a halt with prison officers and lawyers in disputes, stopped the presses of *The Times*, seen firemen and bakers on strike, social workers walk out, Cheshire Homes picketed and patients turned away from hospitals. Those who thought things could not possibly be worse in 1979 were in for an unpleasant surprise.

Over the next few days the snow continued its southward journey and there were falls of six to seven inches in southern Scotland and North-East England. Ahead of the snow the temperature dropped still further and there were savage frosts across England and Wales. On 29 December the winter really began to bite in England. Snow blocked roads throughout Scotland and the north of England and combined with torrential rain to cause serious flooding in Yorkshire. Reservoirs overflowed, Dales rivers burst their banks and the River Ouse rose sixteen feet above normal levels. 'Newly enlisted soldiers' evacuated 500 families in York and laid 3,000 sandbags as flood waters five feet deep covered a large part of the city. Exceptionally high tides in the Humber later in the week threatened more flooding. The Mersey also overflowed in Warrington and the Trent was ten feet above normal and still rising. Meanwhile the AA reported that 600 miles of Pennine roads north of the Peak District were blocked by snow, with only the M62 still open. A County Durham family trying to drive to Cumbria were trapped for ten hours in a snowdrift. Most cross-border roads were also closed, though constant snowploughing kept the A1 open. Blizzards cut off hundreds of small communities in northern Scotland. At Cumbernauld near Glasgow, an elderly man died from exposure after collapsing in a snowstorm. He was found 'on a footpath in a deserted recreation area'.

The rain in the south turned to sleet and then snow and there were further blizzards on 30 December and New Year's Eve, causing the cancellation of many planned celebrations, though the traditional New Year's Day cricket match between the village of Burley in the New Forest and the appropriately named 'Jack Frost XI' went ahead on a pitch cleared of several inches of snow. 'Bottles of whisky, Afghan boots and hot water bottles' helped to keep the cricketers warm. Meanwhile, the AA was reporting that 'The picture is very grim. The snow is covering the whole of Great Britain for the first time since 1963.' In Yorkshire, helicopters rescued dozens of people including forty coach passengers stuck in drifts near Middleton-in-the-Wolds. The Glenlomond mental hospital in Kinross-shire was snowbound and local farmers and volunteers struggled through the drifts with essential supplies.

Roads were blocked from the north of Scotland to Kent, where 500 tourists were unable to reach Dover to catch their ferries because every road was snowbound. At one stage farmer Giles Hadfield 'had 180 marooned men, women and children taking shelter in our house. Their cars and coaches were trapped in drifts eight to ten feet high. During the night we made hundreds of cups of tea; our New Year drinks had gone by 6pm.' 300 passengers were stranded on two trains at Bonneybridge, Stirlingshire, for nine hours, and a hundred passengers on the sleeper from London Paddington to Penzance were trapped by 'a combination of engine failures, frozen points and the weather'.

New Year temperatures had fallen to -7°C at Heathrow, -9°C at Gatwick, -11°C at Benson, Oxfordshire, -16°C at Crawford John in Lanarkshire and -17°C at Linton-on-Ouse in Yorkshire. Flights to and from Heathrow were delayed by up to six hours and British Airways

It's an ill wind... the weather brought a bonanza for breakdown trucks and for plumbers, who were kept busy repairing burst pipes well into Spring.

cancelled thirteen long-haul services. Snow now blanketed much of the northern hemisphere, with the Skane district of southern Sweden declared a 'catastrophe area'. In West Germany, after eighty hours of continuous snow, even army tanks trying to deliver generators to isolated villages became stuck in snowdrifts. Many parts of the United States experienced blizzard conditions and power-cuts affected more than 100,000 people in Dallas, Texas. Undeterred by the appalling weather, hundreds of Muscovites, 'armed with bottles of champagne and vodka', braved temperatures of -35°C to celebrate New Year in Red Square.

In Britain, fifteen London hospitals closed their casualty wards and emergency admissions because of 'staff shortage caused by the weather and sickness'; and more than seventy patients, some seriously ill, were evacuated from two Birmingham hospitals after burst pipes flooded wards. Medical staff in County Durham were having to walk 'up to eight miles' through the snow to reach work because bus services had been halted by the icy conditions, and in Northumberland, farmers were using tractors to ferry nurses through thick snow. Dorset Ambulance Service announced that 'with crews on the point of exhaustion after eighteen hours continuous duty', the service would be restricted to emergency calls only. The Chief Ambulance Officer, John Wilby, said that the weather and 'an acute shortage of petrol' meant that the transport of patients would henceforth have to be 'reviewed daily'. Glasgow ambulances were also only responding to emergency calls.

The RAC called for 'a full investigation into gritting operations throughout the country', after reports that many main roads were not gritted or salted despite forecasts of snow. 'We realise that some local authorities were faced with industrial [action] problems and were unable to get the gritting machines and snowploughs out, but we are anxious to ensure that adequate resources are available to cope with these situations.' Impressions of government competence were not helped by the news that Environment Minister Denis Howell had called

The motorist's nightmare - drifting snow and uncleared roads.

Prime Minister James Callaghan at home to keep him informed of efforts to clear the roads, but 'no one answered the telephone at the Department of the Environment in London.'

By the next day, Mr Howell was fighting back, claiming that in a temperate climate it was not possible 'to have a whole army of men standing by to clear the roads' and saying that local authorities had 'coped quite well' with the snow. A 'Central Operations Unit' at his own ministry had started functioning 'within half a day' of the first reports of heavy snow. Unimpressed, the RAC said that it would be carrying out its own inquiry and claimed that many roads from Manchester and Essex had not been gritted at all, and that gritters in Lothian, Scotland, were not even due to return to work until Thursday 4 January.

The death toll from the weather was climbing rapidly. The body of a seventy-seven year-old man was retrieved from a river in Dulverton, Devon, and Mrs Phyllis Baillie, a widow from Culross, near Dunfermline, was found dead after a fire at her home. Firemen on their way to the blaze were trapped in snowdrifts and though some of them struggled through the snow on foot, Mrs Baillie was already dead when they reached her home. Eighty-six year-old Robert Gunn and his eighty-four year-old wife Jean were found dead in the unheated bedroom of their Glasgow flat. There were further casualties of the snow and ice. At Stanford-le-Hope in Essex, a man was found dead, covered with snow in a car park. Sixty-two year-old Stanley Barriball, 'an eccentric bachelor who always refused to wear a jacket', was found dead 'in his shirtsleeves in a lonely lane' near his home in Lawhitton, Cornwall. A twenty-five year-old policeman, William Pepperell, married for only a year, was killed when his car skidded on an icy road and ploughed into a tree at Dudley in the West Midlands.

In London, three men, David Ennisen, Tony Gray and Charalambos Kourdolis, 'all aged twenty from the Kentish Town area', died when the ice gave way as they were sliding on the frozen "Gentlemen's Bathing Pond" at Hampstead. Two other men, including Mr Gray's brother Laurie, scrambled to safety out of the icy water with the help of rescuers but efforts to rescue the others failed. Martin Cooper, 21, a joiner drinking in a nearby pub, the Freemasons Arms, ran to the pond and pulled himself across the unbroken ice before plunging up to his waist in the frigid water. 'It was unbearably cold,' he said. 'I grabbed a man and manhandled him towards a tree stump where he clung and heaved himself out'. Firemen and police were joined by park-keepers who took boats out to search for the missing men.

At sea, six people, including a girl of twelve, had to jump into the Humber lifeboat from the Dutch ship *Diane V* after the cargo shifted when the ship was struck by a huge wave. Four fishermen from Benfleet in Essex were missing, believed drowned, despite an intensive search by police, coastguards and an air-sea rescue helicopter, and two crewmen of the trawler Ben Asdale were swept to their deaths after it ran aground in a blizzard near Falmouth. The engineer of a Russian factory ship who was helping to repair the trawler's steering gear was also drowned. A thousand people were evacuated from their sea-front homes in Jaywick, Essex, after a freak tide breached the sea wall. At Walton-in-the Naze a 100-foot section of the pier collapsed, and at nearby Clacton, a sixty-foot wave caused a quarter of a million pounds worth of damage to the lifeboat station at the pier. "Suzy Wong", a killer whale kept in the pier's aquarium had to be rescued from 'the fury of the sea' and was taken by road to Windsor Safari Park. A Clacton police spokesman warned of an additional hazard to sea-front sightseers - flying ice. 'Spray from the waves is freezing in the air and razor-sharp slivers of ice are being hurled onto the promenade.'

As Britain began crawling back to work there was the prospect of a fresh round of industrial disputes. Leaders of four public service unions were meeting to discuss co-ordinated action in support of their claim for a £60 a week minimum wage for nearly 1.5 million manual workers and the National Coal Board was considering its reply to the National Union of Mineworkers' forty per cent pay claim. Fuel tanker drivers began their strike, as planned, on 3 January, and lorry drivers started unofficial action, bringing immediate warnings of effects on food supplies. A Road Haulage Association spokesman said that 'within a short time there could be very little food in any shops' - a self-fulfilling prophecy that virtually ensured a wave of panic buying. Coal and milk deliveries were also threatened and it was claimed that the stoppage by lorry drivers delivering newsprint to national and provincial newspapers could 'bring the whole of the newspaper industry to a halt within days'. To complete a miserable New Year it was also announced that people with burst pipes faced waits of several weeks before plumbers could repair them because an industrial dispute at the UBM Mercian builders' merchants had caused 'an acute shortage of copper piping'. Not everyone found the industrial chaos inconvenient; 50,000 children returned to school after the Christmas holidays on 3 January were sent home again the following day because of shortages of heating fuel caused by the strike by tanker drivers.

London commuters returning after the holiday found one third of peak-hour train services had been cancelled. Southern Region's catalogue of woes included 'frozen points, damaged engine cooling systems, staff shortages and rolling stock being in the wrong place.' A French doctor made light of such minor impediments. Finding that he could not drive the twenty-four miles from his Calais home to his work in Boulogne because of snow and abandoned vehicles blocking the roads, he caught the cross-Channel ferry to Dover, and then travelled back across the Channel on another ferry to Boulogne.

He was fortunate not to have been taking the same route to work later that week, for on 4 January 'the worst sea storms and onslaught in living memory', hit the Channel, battering the South Devon villages of Torcross and Beesands. Mountainous seas, driven by Force Ten gales, 'smashed through windows and walls, reducing some buildings to rubble and floating planks of wood'. Houses were left with their roofs 'flapping like paper in the wind'. Fifty foot waves 'picked up massive boulders and hurled them at the helpless seaside communities'. 200 villagers were evacuated from Beesands as 'weeping women recalled that the nearby "sister" village of [South] Hallsands was completely engulfed and destroyed by the sea in 1917.' A police spokesman added, 'We have all aged noticeably down here in the past few hours. Conditions there are appalling, the road between the two seaside villages has collapsed and we have immense difficulties getting essential vehicles into the area.' The route was being made 'additionally hazardous by lorries laden with boulders' to bolster the sea defences. Four loads were taken into Beesands the previous day 'and it is these the sea is hurling back'. Boulders had been piled along the sea-front only yards away from the houses, but 'they stood little chance against waves which towered even over the highest buildings'.

A nineteen year-old Greek seaman, Demetrius Petriphs, was the only survivor of the fifteen-man crew of the 3,000 ton cargo ship *Cantonard*, which sank in mid-Channel off Torbay at the height of the storm. 'The seas had ripped away the weather bulkhead of the bows. I was with the first and second engineers and my mate when we heard the rescue helicopter. We all cheered when the winch came down. I grabbed for it and the friction burnt my hand. I dropped back into the water and suddenly all three of my mates disappeared. I never saw them again.' Mimi Hutchings was lucky to escape with her life after getting away from snowbound Dartmouth by 'hitching a lift' on a French yacht which was then caught in the same storm forty miles off The Lizard in Cornwall. The gales shredded the sails and wrecked the steering gear and the French owner was then washed overboard. With the yacht close to sinking, it was spotted by a merchant ship which radioed for help and Ms Hutchings and the Frenchman's distraught wife were lifted off by an RAF Sea King helicopter moments before the yacht went down.

Elsewhere a furious row over uncleared ice and snow broke out between the British Airports Authority and the seventy-five airlines using Heathrow, led by British Airways, which cancelled all its 350 flights, affecting 18,000 passengers. At a 'strong meeting' the previous evening, BA called the aircraft stands and other areas 'too dangerous to use' and complained of damage to its aircraft and injuries to its staff because of the ice and snow. Some of its aircraft had been trapped on their stands at the airport since New Year's Day. Pan American Airlines' London Director, Martin Sugrue, added that they were 'considering legal action against BAA for negligence and dereliction of duty... There have been near-blizzard conditions in Europe but nowhere has Pan American been experiencing the problems it has at Heathrow.' BAA denied negligence and claimed that in the authority's judgement 130 of the airport's 151 aircraft stands were safe to use. Priority had been given to clearing runways and taxi-ways but by the time this had been done, the snow on the parking stands and around terminal buildings had become 'compacted by the movement of aircraft and vehicles and frozen solid by continuous low temperatures'. As a result, none of the authority's equipment, 'including sixteen snow-clearing vehicles, seven gritting machines and two de-icing lorries' could be used. However, shortly before dawn, BAA brought in 100 labourers and five bulldozers to clear the 'danger areas'.

The situation would have been worse had fresh blizzards expected to hit southern counties not been 'deflected south by cold air over Scandinavia' to ravage the Channel Islands and northern France instead. In East Germany the frost and snow left 300 goods trains snowbound, a situation the Minister for Coal and Energy, Herr Ziergiebel, described as 'a catastrophe'. Street lights in East Berlin were dimmed or extinguished to save power and troops from the twenty-two Russian divisions based in East Germany were called out to help dig people out of stranded vehicles and isolated villages. Soviet television broadcast appeals to save fuel, gas and electricity after temperatures in Moscow fell to -39°C, the lowest point in 100 years. Some areas around Moscow were reported to have been without power and water for two days.

As in previous harsh winters, newspapers were also quick with reports of unseasonably warm weather elsewhere. An Antarctic 'heat wave - relatively speaking' had seen

After weeks of harsh weather, the enthusiasm of amateur snow-clearers began to fade.

temperatures rise to 10°C at the South Pole, Scott and McMurdo Sound bases, the highest temperatures ever recorded there. Back in frigid Britain, there were further reports of fatalities caused by the weather. An eighty-four year-old widow, Mrs Millicent Smith, was found 'dead on a carpet of ice' in the kitchen of her home in Westcliff-on-Sea in Essex. It was believed that she had collapsed from the cold after turning on her kitchen tap, and the water spilling from the sink had frozen over the kitchen floor. The body of a forty-two year-old man, Raymond Hayes, was found in the snow not far from the Coniston Hotel in Sittingbourne, Kent, where he worked, and several fatalities were recorded in car crashes caused by the icy roads.

The next day, a change of direction in the wind brought calming seas and sunshine, and allowed inhabitants of storm-battered Torcross and Beesands to assess the extent of the damage to their villages and homes. As bulldozers shovelled hundreds of tons of shingle out of the streets, 'convoys of lorries of every shape and size' brought 30,000 tons of rock from Plymouth quarries to repair and strengthen the ravaged sea-defences. Several houses had disappeared or been reduced to heaps of rubble. 'A boulder that must have weighed at least a ton was thrown out of the sea', reducing The Start Bay Cafe 'to a heap of iron and stone'. The owner, Paul Stubbs, who evacuated his wife, baby and seventy-four year-old mother from the next-door pub that they also ran, returned to find the contents of that strewn along the sea-front. 'There was a billiard table across the road and two freezers in the street'. All they managed to salvage was 'a few pans and kettles'. One elderly couple at Beesands had refused to leave and sat out the storm unharmed in their tiny sea-front cottage. 'I have lived here all my life,' said seventy-eight year-old John Steel. 'I knew it would be all right in the end.'

Things were getting back to normal too at Heathrow, after 'a large workforce spent a second day and night clearing snow and ice from aircraft parking stands.' But the Saturday sports programme in Britain was 'almost wiped out', with only five of thirty-two FA Cup games 'having any hope of being played', the only rugby union game played was the Scottish trial at Murrayfield, and the only race meeting in the British Isles was at Tramore in County Waterford in Eire.

On Monday 8 January a long-awaited thaw had begun, but it only brought with it problems from burst pipes and flooding. Large parts of Sussex were flooded as dykes around Rye in the Romney Marshes overflowed and the River Ouse burst its banks between Eastbourne and Seaford. If the weather was turning a little more benevolent, the industrial situation was deteriorating rapidly. Pickets from the striking lorry and tanker drivers had succeeded in closing all the country's ports to lorry traffic - prompting the Leader of the Opposition, the little known Margaret Thatcher, to threaten laws to curb union powers - and car drivers queuing at the few petrol stations where there was any fuel to be had, were reported to be paying £5 for three gallons - twice the normal price. Greater Manchester's buses were kept off the roads all weekend to save fuel, 30,000 children in Northamptonshire were told to stay away from school and it was a similar picture at schools throughout the country. The National Consumers' Association warned housewives panic-buying food that they were 'cutting their own throats; panic-buying causes shortages and shortages push up prices.' The news that 'many grocers and supermarkets will be forced to close next week because of dwindling food supplies' was scarcely calculated to improve the situation. A National Farmers Union spokesman was meanwhile warning of 'famine' on British farms and widespread livestock deaths if deliveries of animal feed were not resumed by lorry drivers.

Construction companies paralysed by the big freeze, hired their earthmoving equipment out as makeshift snowploughs.

The next day tanker drivers voted to accept a pay offer of thirteen to fifteen per cent, but 180,000 road haulage workers moved closer to all-out official strike action after the employers refused to raise their 13.2 per cent pay offer, and the train drivers added to the chaos by announcing that they too would be undertaking industrial action from 16 January. Schools already hit by shortages of heating oil were now being closed by burst pipes and flooded classrooms. 900 schools were shut, with Sussex, Surrey, Buckinghamshire, Humberside, Lincolnshire and Yorkshire the worst affected counties.

The slow thaw continued in the South though north-westerly gales brought torrential rain and hail, but in the Midlands, North and Scotland it fell as snow with the fierce winds whipping up fresh drifts. Eighty-three Glasgow buses were trapped in drifts at one point. The Selsey lifeboat was called out to rescue nineteen crew and a woman passenger from a Panamanian ship which lost a propeller in the storm.

By the next day there were reports that drivers in the Midlands were 'abandoning their cars, not because of snow, but because there was no petrol to be had at any price.' Even though most tanker drivers had now returned to work, Texaco drivers were still out on strike and were successfully picketing the other fuel depots in the region. Those turning to the train instead were warned that talks between British Rail and the train drivers' unions had broken down, guaranteeing that the strike set for 16 January would go ahead. Taking to the air provided no refuge either; Glasgow Airport was closed because the lorry drivers' strike had prevented deliveries of de-icing fluid and it had now run out.

Some even more precious fluids were in short supply in Scotland on 14 January, with reports that beer in many pubs had frozen as temperatures fell as low as -24.6°C, and that there was a shortage of blood in many hospitals. Only once in the entire century had a

Snow-blowers imported from Scandinavia were a new weapon in the road-clearers' armoury but even they were powerless against the biggest drifts, which could only be moved by JCBs or dynamite.

marginally lower temperature been recorded. Many train, bus and air services were cancelled, diesel went "waxy" in the cold and would not flow at the pumps and with the sea icebound at Oban 'confused seagulls' could be seen 'to wander over frozen waves'. The savage cold saw the load on the South of Scotland's electricity supply exceed 4,400 megawatts, well above the previous peak in 1976-77.

In the midst of this misery, the hordes of striking workers were joined by a one-day stoppage by ambulancemen and the railway network then ground to a halt, not because of snow, but the threatened twenty-four hour walk-out by 28,000 train drivers. Lorry drivers were meanwhile still picketing and claims by Agriculture Minister John Silkin that eighty per cent of food supplies were getting through were greeted with derision by food manufacturers. A spokesman for Britain's biggest manufacturer of margarine and fats, Van den Bergh, said it 'hadn't made a delivery in a fortnight apart from small amounts to hospitals and schools'.

"The winter of discontent" was now really gathering pace. Eight million Londoners were again left without ambulance services for twenty-four hours on 19 January and a spokesman for the striking ambulancemen, Bill Dunn, was universally condemned for his comments on their refusal even to answer emergency calls: 'If it means lives are lost, that is how it must be. This time we are determined that the capital will take notice of what we are saying.' There was further cheerful news with the announcement that a Day of Action by 1.5 million public service workers planned for 22 January would affect burials, rubbish disposal, schools, hospital treatments and operations.

On 21 January snow returned, bringing widespread disruption once more. Dartmoor, Exmoor and Portland in Dorset were again cut off and air traffic at Heathrow disrupted. At midnight that night the snow-clearing crews at the airport joined other public service workers in staging the "Day of Action" - a twenty-four hour strike. Hostile public reaction and pressure from Bill Dunn's own colleagues saw the ambulancemen's ban on emergency calls lifted but other ambulance services remained affected and every public service from airports to rubbish tips was shut down. *The Times* would have been expected to produce a ferocious editorial ... except that it was itself in the midst of a twelve month "lock-out" that heralded the beginning of the end for the old Fleet Street and a move by News International to a non-union plant at Wapping. Talks to end the lorry drivers' dispute broke down and after a one-day strike on 23 January by train drivers, their union leader, Ray Buckton, walked out of talks with the British Railways Board and announced another twenty-four hour stoppage two days later. The ugliness of the industrial situation was shown by the news that sixty-five patients from a Birmingham cancer ward were sent home because of action by pickets of the National Union of Public Employees, and a hospital official claimed that a patient needing 'urgent treatment for a spinal disease' had been turned away from the hospital by pickets. Surgeon Mr Patrick Chesterman staged his own one-man protest at his outpatients clinic at Battle Hospital, Reading, by turning away anyone who was a union member. 'I decided it was time someone in this country hit back at the unions', he said, 'instead of taking everything lying down.'

Government figures showed that unemployment had now increased by 91,000 in a single month, with the blame laid equally on the strikes and the snow. There was plenty more of both to come. A fresh blizzard swept the country on 23 January, dumping four inches of snow on London, seven inches on the West Country and a foot of snow on parts of Wales.

The search for an aircraft missing after crashing into the sea five miles off Dungeness on the Kent coast was abandoned as hopes faded for the lives of the five people aboard. Heathrow, Gatwick and half a dozen other airports were closed, and conditions on the roads were described as 'horrific', 'incredibly dangerous', 'atrocious' and 'diabolical', with abandoned cars 'littering' roads. As cars ploughed into each other in 'a chaotic spate' of accidents, thirty mile-an-hour speed limits were imposed across most of the motorway network. Nonetheless police patrols reported that many drivers were travelling at speeds of seventy miles an hour or more.

There were twenty-mile tailbacks on the M1 and travelling into London by car became so difficult that employees who rang their work were told 'Don't worry, turn around and go home'. Thousands did so, 'including jurors and witnesses at trials which had to be delayed or abandoned'. Branches of the major banks and some stores closed because of staff shortages, many schools were shut and many areas were without phone-lines after the weight of snow brought poles and lines down. In total it was estimated that about half of the eight million office, shop and service industry employees in the South-East took the day off and the pattern was repeated throughout the country as the rail strike and snow turned Britain into what the RAC termed 'a white hell'.

The one-day strike by train drivers made the effects of the weather even worse, and British Rail warned that the legacy would be felt the next day as well, particularly for commuters. 'Because no trains have been running today, heavy ice deposits have built up on conductor rails. While every effort will be made to get the lines open, our advice is not to rely on commuter services.' The one piece of cheering news was that a Boeing 707 carrying luxury goods and cases of whisky for the notorious Ugandan dictator Idi Amin and his entourage, had hit a patch of ice and skidded off the runway at Stansted when making the biweekly "whisky run" to Kampala. The Ugandan Airlines plane was buried up to its engines in snow, ploughed up by the skid.

The forecast chaos on the railways, particularly British Rail's Southern Region, duly arrived the following day with hundreds of thousands of commuters stranded when the majority of services into London were cancelled because no de-icing had been possible on frozen points and conductor rails because of the previous day's strike. The few trains that ran were so full that many passengers were left on the platforms. At East Croydon, 'the crowd on the platform was fourteen-deep.' Most commuters still made efforts to get to work. Victoria Underground station was so overcrowded that it was closed to ease the pressure, buses were 'packed' and journeys that normally took thirty minutes were lasting two and a half hours. Sixteen year-old Shirley Billis showed extraordinary determination not to miss her day's work as a Fleet Street secretary. Leaving her home in Abbey Wood at 7.15am, she arrived at her office 'five and a quarter hours later and £7 poorer' having taken a taxi from Woolwich to Charing Cross. The railways were restored to some sort of order by the end of the day, just in time for the start of the next twenty-four hour strike by train drivers, so nobody got to work by train at all that day.

Council gritters were on strike in Southwark where 'ambulances were busy picking up people, mostly elderly, who had been injured by falling on icy pavements.' In Liverpool, health authorities announced plans to open 'an emergency mass mortuary' in a disused factory to cope with the ever-growing number of bodies left unburied because of the strike by gravediggers and crematorium staff. Anthony Steen, Conservative MP for Wavertree, said

Two kids making first use of a fresh fall of snow in a city park.

there were 'already more than 100 corpses in Liverpool mortuaries' and it was proposed that bodies should be 'embalmed before being stored in polythene bags'. Much of Greater Manchester faced the same problem and clergymen in Tameside issued an appeal to strikers to return to work because of the suffering being caused to bereaved families. Barry Shuttleworth, Birmingham Divisional Officer of the National Union of Public Employees, responded to such appeals by remarking that 'there is no point in bringing people out, if they are not going to have any effect'.

On Thursday 25 January there were further heavy snowfalls - seven inches fell in Birmingham and eight inches in Ulster in less than an hour. Commuters forced onto the roads by the latest twenty-four hour rail strike endured 'blizzard-like conditions' in the Thames Valley and North London as they tried to reach work. As gales and snowstorms swept over London, the Society of West End Theatres, already badly hit by the effects of the rail strikes, admitted that they were 'certainly feeling the draught' from the cold weather.

The next morning the train drivers returned to work but black ice had now 'paralysed' Britain's motorways with more than 300 miles of the M5, M6, M42 and M69 'in a hazardous condition' made worse by industrial action by road-gritting crews. A thirty-mile section of the M6 in Staffordshire was closed in both directions, and approach roads at Junction 10 of the

*The start of one of the most notorious stretches of road in bad weather
- the Stainmore Pass linking Durham and Westmorland (now Cumbria).*

M1 in Hertfordshire were shut when black ice 'made it impossible for vehicles to get on or off the motorway'. A thirty-mile stretch of the A34 from the M4 motorway to beyond Oxford was also closed and the M2 was restricted to one lane at the London end because of drifting snow, which was also causing havoc on the M1 and M62 in Yorkshire.

As the blizzards moved on, temperatures dropped. On the night of 27 to 28 January, the temperature at Coltishall in Norfolk fell to -15°C, the lowest ever recorded there. As if shopkeepers did not have enough to worry about with thick snow, arctic temperatures and dwindling supplies of both food and customers, the National Chamber of Trade issued a warning on Monday 29 January that shopkeepers should either 'make a perfect job' of clearing snow from outside their premises or leave it untouched. Having consulted legal opinion, they warned that 'if someone slips on untouched snow, even on your land, he has no action against you. Once you have taken a broom or shovel to it, even on the public footpath, you make yourself liable. If you leave a small patch of ice or snow and someone slips, he can sue you.' The Daily Telegraph meanwhile, not normally noted for its admiration of the Soviet Union, remarked that 'in Moscow, where they know about snow, public authorities are required to have roads and footpaths cleared by daybreak', and suggested that Britain's councils and government could do worse than take a leaf out of their book.

Meanwhile snow continued to fall from Wales, the Midlands and East Anglia northwards, with fog, sleet and freezing rain causing similar chaos further south. The AA advised motorists 'not to go out unless it was necessary, and then to keep to main roads' and the RAC warned that 'a combination of fog and black ice, added to lack of proper road gritting through industrial troubles, is a lethal mixture and the greatest care is needed in braking and cornering'. The A1 was closed south of Berwick, the M62 was the only trans-Pennine road open and more than 100 miles of the M6 in Lancashire and Cumbria had a forty mile-an-hour speed restriction because of blizzards and drifting snow. In Scotland the A77 was blocked at Glen App, Strathclyde, the A719 at Dunure, and the A822 at Crieff in Tayside. Ulster police warned that the M1 and M2 were 'treacherous' because of snow and black ice and many other roads were blocked. Farmers with tractors were called in to reach twelve cars trapped in drifts near Alnwick in Northumberland. Most of the cars were towed to safety but others could not be moved and their occupants were driven away in tractors.

The accumulations of snow triggered avalanches in Snowdonia and the Pennines, causing injuries and deaths. Stephen Hornsby, 26, of Stockport was killed when an avalanche near Saddleworth in Lancashire swept him 100 feet down a quarry face. His twin brother Phillip, was with him but escaped uninjured. A third member of the party, Judith Moffitt, 34, from South Shields, Tyne and Wear, suffered a broken leg. A woman fell 150 feet to her death from a rock face during a snowstorm at Llanymynech, Shropshire. Her husband who was with her, was unhurt. Several other injured hikers and climbers were brought in by mountain rescue teams, including a fifteen year-old boy who collapsed while hiking on the Pennine Way north of Crowden.

The month ended as the third coldest January of the century in England and Wales - only 1940 and 1963 were colder. And although February began with a brief thaw, bringing rain and flooding to much of lowland England and Wales, with exceptionally high tides on the East Coast threatening further problems, elsewhere it was the mixture as before. Leeds householders were told to boil their drinking water after a strike by members of the General and Municipal Workers Union meant that drinking water was not receiving 'normal treatment' at the waterworks. One businessman was delighted by the problems, since sales of his imported French bottled water were up 500 per cent. He had started selling the water after drinking it on a holiday in France. 'Many people thought it was a daft idea when I started selling the water,' he said, 'but they now appreciate it.'

Mortgage rates were rising to record levels, unions representing 100,000 British Leyland workers gave strike notice to the company, disgruntled Southern Region commuters were told that there was 'no solution' to disruptions caused by snow and ice - there were 15,000 sets of points and thousands of miles of conductor rail that could be affected by icing - and Liverpool health authorities were now warning that they might have to start burying bodies at sea if striking gravediggers didn't return to work soon. 200 bodies had been embalmed and stored in a temporary mortuary in an empty electrical factory, but the city had another sixty bodies that couldn't be embalmed because post-mortems had been carried out or the embalming process was 'technically impossible', and these were causing serious concern. Work had also stopped at cemeteries in St Helens, Widnes, Southport, Tameside - where forty bodies were awaiting burial - and at Southwark in London.

Refuse disposal was at a standstill. In Soho plastic bags of rubbish were piled 'fifteen feet high' and a restaurant owner said he had, 'seen rats as big as rabbits running among the rubbish.' One bemused American visitor remarked, 'I don't know what you're moaning about. We see this every day in Chicago', but other tourists were 'making a beeline for Leicester Square to take photographs' of the mounds of rubbish. Councils laid rat poison at their tips and 'sprayed them with deodorant', but at Tower Hamlets, councillors had other things to worry about and were forced to meet 'at a secret rendezvous' after striking employees locked them out of the Town Hall.

Hospitals were also badly affected by industrial action, including a four-hour lightning strike at Great Ormond Street Children's Hospital. Westminster Hospital appealed for volunteers to replace its striking workers and got far more than the seventy a day they needed, but other hospitals - and seventeen in Central London were 'facing shutdown' - did not follow suit, 'for fear of exacerbating the situation' with their striking workforce. There was a demonstration of one possible result of exacerbation at Westminster, where an ambulance and a hospital van had their tyres slashed. The Leader of the Opposition, Margaret Thatcher, told her preferred confidant, Jimmy Young, on his Radio 2 programme that she 'wouldn't mind taking on trade unions who inflicted damage and suffering on the sick and elderly'. And even Prime Minister James "Sunny Jim" Callaghan complained of 'free collective vandalism' by the striking hospital workers, and called for them to return to work, saying that 'the denial of food and proper attention to sick human beings was not acceptable in any community'.

As February began, the weather outlook was equally miserable. Rain blanketing the South fell as snow in the North caused further transport chaos. When the M62 had been built, it was designed so that the prevailing winds would sweep the carriageways clear of snow, making it Britain's first "weatherproof road". Unfortunately the designers had failed to include in their calculations the consequences of industrial action by men driving gritting lorries, and as the snow fell on frozen, untreated roads, thirty-five miles of the M62 had to be closed. Five teenage girls and three teachers from a girls' home in St Helens had to be rescued from the 1,500 foot Winter Hill near Bolton after being caught in gales and driving snow. By 3 February, the Daily Telegraph was crowing about 'conditions worthy of Spring' in the South, while the North was in the grip of yet more fresh blizzards.

Although drifts still blocked hundreds of roads, there was then a lull in the storms for a week, persuading some that the worst of the winter - at least in meteorological terms - might be behind them. On the industrial front, each thaw in relations in one industry was immediately followed by the onset of permafrost in another. There were the first chinks of light in the dispute with gravediggers and crematorium workers when two gravediggers in Spennymoor, County Durham, were shamed into returning to work after two families began digging graves for their own dead relatives. And in a masterly public relations coup, crematorium workers and gravediggers in Plymouth offered to allow funerals to go ahead providing that the city's undertakers and clergy gave their own services free. Any PR benefits were immediately torpedoed by the news that Delysia English, the thirty-four year-old mother of murdered teenager Jeanette English, had been unable to visit her daughter's grave because the gates of Hampstead Cemetery were locked because of the cemetery workers' dispute. 'All I wanted to do was kneel by the grave, say a simple prayer and lay a few flowers', Mrs English said. Perhaps wisely, officials of the National Union of Public Employees declined to comment.

Elsewhere, a strike by school caretakers saw half a million children sent home. Although a 'revolt of the moderates' at British Leyland on 9 February saw 67,000 of the company's 94,000 workers and twenty-seven of its thirty-three plants vote against an all-out strike over productivity targets, without the components produced at the other six plants production would grind to a halt anyway. Meanwhile pickets at Leyland's Longbridge plant erected barbed wire barricades to stop builders getting to work on the site of the new Mini factory.

Many motorists gave up the unequal struggle, abandoned their cars and walked.

Faced with opinion polls that showed Mrs Thatcher holding a lead of between eleven and twenty percentage points over him, Prime Minister James Callaghan finally conceded, during an interview with Llew Gardner on Thames Television's *TV Eye* programme, that he had 'seriously misjudged the mood of the country'. He offered an unusual defence of his actions and inactions: 'I am not an archangel.' Even his predecessor, Harold Wilson, joined in the chorus of criticism, blaming much of the government's problems on Callaghan's 'nailing five per cent to the mast' over public sector pay claims. In an effort to buy industrial peace before terminal damage was done to his chances in the May General Election, Callaghan now gave tacit approval to ten per cent pay rises for council workers in the "dirty jobs" dispute, but any increases above that level would have to be funded from the councils' own resources. He also announced a pact with the unions to bring peace back to industrial relations; it was immediately denounced by Mrs Thatcher as 'a boneless wonder'.

After the brief lull on the weather front, winter swept in once more with renewed vigour. Gales pounded the coasts and 'freak waves estimated at forty to sixty feet high' destroyed houses and flooded a Naval helicopter base at Portland in Dorset. Around 100 families had to be rescued from their flooded homes and taken to a local school serving as an emergency evacuation centre. 'Distraught and weeping women, clutching children, were plucked from rooms six feet deep with swirling sea water and taken to safety in a convoy of small boats.' Naval personnel rescued a three-week-old baby from one house. A police sergeant with twenty years' service in the region said, 'Undoubtedly this is the worst attack by the sea in living memory; none of us have known anything like it. Waves up to sixty feet high enveloped

Millions of gallons of milk were poured down the drain, for tanker-drivers often could not get through to outlying farms for days and weeks on end.

rows of houses 200 yards back from the beach. Most of them are so badly damaged they will probably never be lived in again. It's really heartbreaking to look at homes just bought or built up over a lifetime smashed to smithereens, reduced to rubble and bits of floating debris.'

The island was totally cut off from the mainland with the only road - Chesil Beach Road - 'badly subsided and practically impassable'. The primary gas main was ruptured by the pounding seas, cars and lorries were being 'washed down the street and people bowled over by surging waves'. Some families vowed never to return. Alec and Jenny Wellman were woken by the sound of 'huge oil drums, propelled by thundering sea water smashing down their front door'. A neighbour's car was also hurled against the front of their house. Margaret Pay, licensee of the Little Ship Inn, told a reporter by telephone, 'As I speak to you, breeze blocks are coming through the wall. The water is still coming over. I won't be here for the next high tide - I've had enough.'

The next day - Valentine's Day - fresh blizzards swept the country. On the M1 in Northamptonshire, high winds blew four high-sided lorries over onto the central reservation - all four drivers escaped with bruises and shock. A twenty mile-an-hour speed limit was imposed on the M1 in Nottinghamshire and Derbyshire, and police closed part of the A17 between Sleaford and Newark because it was 'just a sheet of ice'. All trans-Pennine roads, including the M62, were closed, with queues on the motorway 'stretching for miles' either side of the summit at Windy Hill. 200 people spent the night at the Hartshead Moor service station and in the nearby city of Bradford the three-star Victoria Hotel set up a '£2.50 a night dormitory' in the hotel ballroom to accommodate 100 people, both travellers and city workers unable to get home.

1,000 Southern Region commuters spent an unromantic nine hours trapped in two iced-up trains. The 6am Ramsgate to Victoria train and the 6.45am Faversham to Cannon Street, both lost power because of ice on the conductor rails. 'Heavy diesels' were eventually brought up and they pulled the trains into Rochester just before 3.30pm. Passengers on two other trains from Ramsgate and Dover eventually reached London, but they arrived almost five and a half hours late.

There were abandoned cars and lorries 'all over the place' in the South-East, according to the AA, and a lightning strike by gritting workers in the Folkestone, Hythe and Romney Marsh areas added to the problems. In Suffolk, 200 people who had to abandon their cars in drifts, were accommodated in Bury St Edmunds' Guildhall.

A blizzard also trapped 250 motorists on the roof of the Pennines at the notorious Stainmore Summit on the A66, where dozens of cars were abandoned after a furniture van was blown over by the winds, blocking the road. The static vehicles were rapidly buried in snow drifts. Council workmen on the Cumbrian side of the border suspended their overtime ban to drive snowploughs and enabled the stranded motorists to be ferried away in police and army Land Rovers. They were taken to Appleby and spent the night in the village hall. Some got away by public transport the next day, but fresh blizzards condemned 107 of them to a second night there. Many cars and lorries remained stranded on Stainmore for several days and, like Cornish wreckers, some enterprising locals took advantage of the unexpected bounty offered by these victims of the storms, forcing police, whenever the weather permitted, to mount patrols to deter looting.

In the Cheviots, three men 'cheated death in a twelve-hour ordeal' after their light aircraft was forced down and crashed in the blizzard. Despite blinding snow, two of them - Jim Winning, 35, and Findlay Guild, 27 - set off to find help for their injured colleague, Peter Hart, 27, and the unconscious pilot, Mervyn Donnell, 51, who later died. 'Conditions were good when we started', Mr Guild said, 'but we got into a blizzard and then just ran into a mountain.' Jim Winning added, 'It was just like a white-out. We couldn't even see the wing-tips before the crash. Then the instruments started to ice up and the altimeter stuck at 2,330 feet. We were semi-conscious and sat there for three hours before setting out for help. Twice a rescue helicopter passed over without seeing us.' They struggled through the snow for ninety minutes before stumbling across an unoccupied farmhouse, where they warmed themselves and found some fresh clothing. They then pressed on for another three hours, eventually finding a small, occupied farm, near Wooler. An RAF helicopter was on its way to pick up the injured man 'within minutes', but the pilot's body was not recovered until the next day.

In Cumbria, Helen Sherlock, 40, was rescued by helicopter after spending twenty hours trapped in her car when trying to make her way home to Newcastle from Nenthead near Alston. She was later said to be 'satisfactory' in hospital. A premature baby weighing only two pounds was born at home in Haversham, Suffolk, after ambulances failed to get through the snow to take the mother to hospital. A doctor and policemen were 'in attendance'. A number of villages near Saffron Walden in East Anglia were cut off by widespread flooding and 'roads covered by sheet ice'.

After the fresh snowfalls, the National Farmers Union was now warning that thousands of upland sheep marooned by snowdrifts were starving to death. Roads had been blocked on and off for well over a month and with lambing time due the situation was 'getting critical'. The weather continued to deteriorate with further blizzards over the next four days 'paralysing Britain'. Easterly gales 'scything from Scandinavia and Poland' piled up drifts up to twenty feet deep. Conditions on British Rail's Eastern Region were said to be the worst since 1947. 1,200 stranded vehicles blocked the M180 and M181 in Humberside, the only road open out of Scotland was the A1, and 400 stranded motorists, including the thirty-strong cast of the touring musical *The Desert Song*, were looked after at RAF Wittering after becoming stuck on the A1 and the A47. Motorists on both sides of the Pennines were advised to stay at home and Lincolnshire police warned people not to go out 'unless it is a matter of life and death'. Drivers who insisted on going out were advised by the RAC to take 'a mini survival kit containing a blanket, a shovel and a flask of coffee.' Checker Cabs of Colchester faced accusations of profiteering after making their own bad weather arrangements by tripling all fares. 'These fares are justified,' a spokesman for the company claimed. 'Every time a driver goes out in these conditions, he is risking his car which may be worth £6,000.'

The RAF was asked to airlift miners' union leader Arthur Scargill to a debate at the Oxford Union on the motion that 'private enterprise has failed the British economy', but had to decline because all helicopters were on emergency standby, and for the first time in the 108 year history of the FA Cup, the weather wiped out an entire round of cup ties. Virtually the only sports fixture going on anywhere in the British Isles was the rugby union international at Lansdowne Road, Dublin. In Norfolk, ambulances were unable to reach fifteen year-old Alison Smith, who needed vital kidney treatment, and the conditions also made an airlift impossible. Instead, with two other kidney patients, she was carried thirty-five miles through the Norfolk Broads by the Gorleston lifeboat and eventually reached hospital in Norwich. The lifeboat also picked up three British Rail employees stranded at Reedham after fighting their way through the snow from Great Yarmouth to open the swing bridges for the lifeboat. Nightworkers at a British Sugar Corporation factory at Cantley in Norfolk were also rescued by boat after being stranded for two days. The coaster *Locatur* picked them up and took them forty miles down river to Great Yarmouth.

Elsewhere in Norfolk, it took four snowploughs, one JCB, an ambulance and an escort of police cars to get twenty year-old Kim Pooley through the snow to hospital after she was taken ill with appendicitis. Helicopters managed to pick up two stranded expectant mothers. Mrs Susan Brooks was picked up from Thrigby after helicopter pilot Captain Bill Barrell battled through blinding snow and was guided in by a bonfire lit in a field. A helicopter from RAF Coltishall also made a successful pick-up of a pregnant woman from Hempnall, but in Lincolnshire a woman from Broxholme gave birth in an ambulance as she was being rushed to hospital. It took the ambulance three hours to reach her, and the driver had to struggle the last few hundred yards on foot through waist-high snowdrifts after the ambulance and a police car got stuck.

All three women's children were born safely, but there was a less happy outcome for twins born prematurely in the middle of the blizzard, who both died after the ambulance taking them to hospital became trapped in drifts at Bunns Bank, Aldeburgh. A second ambulance, carrying incubators, was sent eighteen miles to try and save them, but arrived too late. Another baby, Lisa Benson, born prematurely in the cut-off town of Haverhill in Suffolk, was

Even where pubs were not snowbound, they were often forced to close because delivery wagons could not get through to them with fresh supplies of beer and food.

eventually airlifted to University College Hospital in London, but died soon afterwards. In Oxfordshire the driver and passengers of a Morris 1800 died after colliding with an army petrol tanker on ungritted roads at Gore Hill, near Chilton. In Bristol a pedestrian was killed after being trapped under a skidding van and two men died and another was seriously injured in Loughborough after a bus slid off a snow-covered road and hit the queue of people waiting to board.

The fresh storms led Hannah Hauxwell, owner of Low Birk Hatt fFarm in Baldersdale, County Durham and famous as the eccentric star of the Yorkshire Television documentary *Too Long A Winter*, to remark that 'This is the worst winter I have ever experienced. Last week was the roughest. On the Tuesday the electricity went off and it didn't come on again until Thursday. The wind got up and created a sort of whirlwind with the snow. Round here we call it "stouring". There was a roaring round the house... that was a bit frightening. While the electricity was off, I stayed in bed as long as I could, wearing all my woolly jumpers, my socks and a tweed coat. I couldn't heat water for my hot-water bottles - I like my bottles - and I couldn't make tea. I made myself corned beef sandwiches and drank cold water.'

The owners of the Tan Hill Inn, "Britain's highest inn" a few miles to the south, on the Pennine border between Cumbria, Durham and North Yorkshire, were once more cut off, and in total were 'snowed in for all but five days between New Year's Eve and April Fool's Day'. Snowdrifts buried the building up to the first floor windows and in between the blizzards, freezing rain covered every exposed surface in a two-inch layer of ice. While trying to move a generator that was frozen to the ground, the landlord slipped and broke his front teeth on the casing.

'For a week, I drank soup and bottled Guinness through a straw, yelling blue murder every time cold air hit my exposed teeth. When the weather at last cleared, I set off to walk the five miles to the edge of the moor - the road had been dug out to there by snow-blowers and JCBs - dragging a sledge behind me to fetch supplies. Some of the drifts must have been well over twenty feet deep, completely filling stream-beds and gullies, and when I reached the lane at the edge of the moor I was walking level with the tops of the walls because the road was completely buried under the drifts. A kindly farmer gave me a lift to a dentist in Barnard Castle, and having got a temporary repair to my teeth and bought as many groceries as I could fit on my sledge, I towed it back over the snow to Tan Hill, arriving exhausted just as the sun was going down.'

After being blocked in for six weeks, a snow-blower finally broke through to them. They jumped in the car and followed him back down the road to Reeth in Swaledale, 'bouncing between the banks of hard-packed snow as if we were tobogganing on the Cresta Run. We filled the boot with groceries and set off back to the inn. The wind was already blowing the snow back into the road as we drove up there and by nightfall we were once more cut off.'

On 15 February, the Callaghan government, accused of paralysis in the face of the country's industrial strife and desperate to be seen to be doing something about the weather, if nothing else, now called in the avuncular figure of Denis Howell. Drafted in as "Minister for Drought" during the prolonged dry summer of 1976, Howell was now reincarnated as

Even Land Rovers needed a tow.

Snowplough crews worked all night to try and keep roads open. Wild creatures, like the rabbit in the foreground, foraged for whatever food they could find, but millions of birds and animals starved or froze to death.

"Minister for Snow" and told to 'drop all other duties and co-ordinate efforts to keep the nation moving'. He was reported to be considering calling in troops to grit the roads and reminded councils of their 'obligations' to keep roads open, saying that help was available if needed. However, he turned a deaf ear to appeals to declare a State of Emergency and when asked what his immediate plans were, said, 'Well, I've offered my prayers to the Almighty - we'll have to wait and see if there's a response.' There almost was, as the helicopter carrying him on a visit to 'badly-hit Sheffield', almost collided with a private plane over Hertfordshire. There was more grim news for government and public with coal and electricity prices set to rise by nine per cent and inflation reaching 9.3 per cent, fuelled by the soaring price of foodstuffs because of the bad weather, but there was one straw to clutch at, with the suggestion that the long-running "dirty jobs" dispute with council manual workers was 'likely to be over' by Monday 19 February.

Peterborough Council did not wait for that, and that weekend called in private contractors to grit the roads after their twenty-five striking drivers had demanded £50,000 - albeit paid to charity - to suspend their own industrial action to do so. After the private contractors were brought in, the National Union of Public Employees announced that the council's entire 400-strong manual workforce would strike in retaliation. The news that a quarter of a million civil servants would be walking out in a separate pay dispute later that week caused rather less alarm to the public and led some comedians to speculate whether anyone would notice.

The AA meanwhile reported that dozens of main roads in Cambridgeshire, East Anglia,

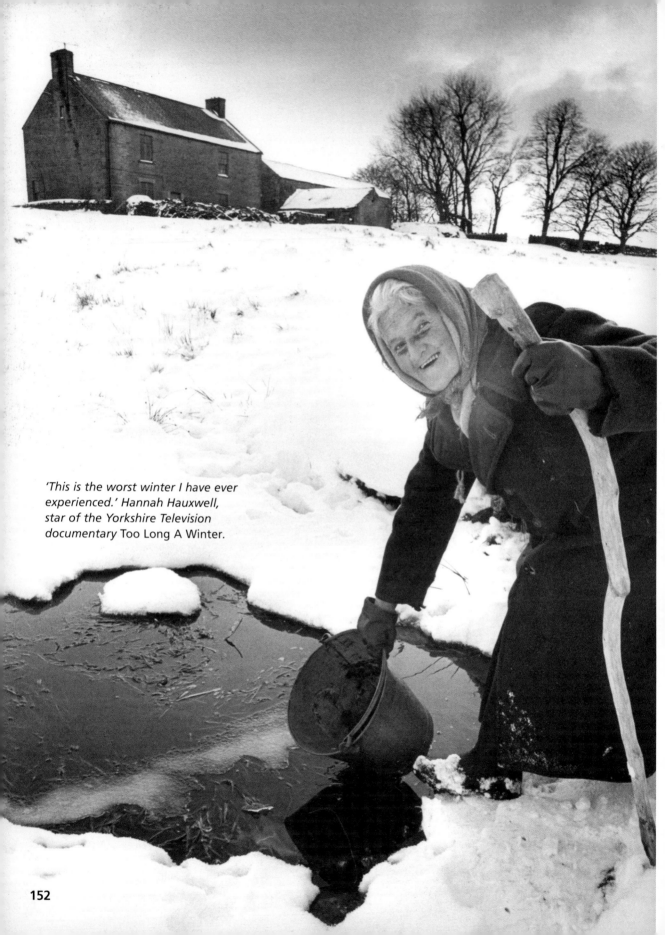

'This is the worst winter I have ever experienced.' Hannah Hauxwell, star of the Yorkshire Television documentary Too Long A Winter.

152

"The Winter of Discontent" - Pedestrians are forced to pick their way over mounds of stinking rubbish dumped in a Glaswegian alleyway.

the Midlands and the North were still blocked by snow, and in Scotland a combined police and AA operation rescued sixty people, including twelve children, trapped in their cars by thirteen-foot snowdrifts near Dalwhinnie in the Grampians. With visibility in the blinding snow down to seven feet, the rescuers had to abandon their vehicles on the A9 Stirling to Inverness road and struggle through the snow for three miles in the gathering darkness, before 'probing through the snow with steel rods by torchlight' to find the abandoned vehicles. Some drivers, especially those with young children, opted to stay in sleeping bags in their cars rather than struggle in white-out visibility to Dalwhinnie. Once more the newspapers could not help pointing the contrast between Britain's chaos and the situation in Moscow, where despite temperatures of -30°C, 'everything was running like clockwork' according to a Thomson Holidays rep looking after 260 British holidaymakers. Meanwhile in China, the *Peking Daily* had more serious problems to deal with, after identifying 'yellow bell-bottom trousers' - the Chinese preferred to call them 'trumpet trousers' - 'long hair for boys' and 'fancy knitted caps' as a new threat to the morals of Chinese youth. 'How can this sort of thing help modernisation and socialist construction?' a correspondent of the *People's Daily* asked.

Back in Britain, on 23 February troops broke through to Cam Houses Farm near Hawes in Wensleydale, where farmer Robert Middleton and his family had been cut off since Christmas. He had broken his leg in December and had it put in plaster, but the snow had prevented him from going to hospital to have the plaster removed. His wife Susan related that

Even where the snowploughs managed to get through,
abandoned vehicles caused ongoing problems.

he had telephoned his doctor, who told him he could take the plaster off himself, 'so he cut his leg out with a hacksaw'. Once a way had been opened to the farm, Mrs Middleton set off for the shops in the nearest town of Hawes, accompanied by her daughter Helen, 4, and riding on an army Scorpion tank. Men of the Royal Scots Dragoon Guards 'who took *Amazing Grace* to the top of the hit parade' - worked through the night to deliver six tons of fodder for the Middleton's starving sheep, and they left behind a souvenir, another Scorpion tank that became stuck in a huge snowdrift near the farm and 'will probably have to stay there until the snow melts'. At the hamlet of Booze in Arkengarthdale a few miles to the north, troops used two twenty-ton diggers to cut a way through to three similarly isolated farms and take food to the farmers and fodder for their stock.

Like the weather, the industrial situation showed little sign of a thaw. With election day only a few weeks away, Prime Minister James Callaghan offered the National Coal Board a government subsidy to help them meet the cost of a settlement of the miners' forty per cent pay claim, but the next dispute was never far away. On the same day teachers' unions decided on a pay claim of 36.5 per cent, and when manual workers at three London hospitals went back after a twelve day strike, they promptly walked out again because the work areas they were returning to had not been properly cleaned. An IRA "bomb-blitz" on Yeovil on 23 February merely added to the air of crisis, and fear of the "Yorkshire Ripper", still prowling the streets despite a massive police investigation and thousands of calls from the public with information, was an added stress on women, particularly in the North of England.

On 5 March there were the first signs of spring, with the temperature in London rising to 12°C and day-trippers packing the beaches at Eastbourne, Brighton and Hastings, but the Northern winter continued, with hail and snow in Scotland and floods in Yorkshire. When the River Ouse burst its banks at York, 180 guests at the Victory Hotel had to be hastily evacuated.

On Saturday 17 March, with British Summer Time beginning that night, heavy snow once again began falling throughout Britain, with blizzard conditions as far south as Sussex. Many new-born lambs were killed. 'They never even had a chance to stand up,' one Cumbrian farmer ruefully remarked. The news that the fox-hunting season had been 'the worst for years' was a less universal cause for regret. Anglesey was without power for thirty hours after power lines collapsed under the weight of snow, and in Wiltshire lightning blew a crater in the grounds of Marlborough College and 'blasted open a sewer, hurling a manhole cover several feet into the air'. In North Wales, Shon Devey, a twenty-six year-old climber, spent the night on Cader Idris near Dolgellau. He not only survived but, to outward appearances at least, also disproved the local legend that 'anyone who spends the night on the mountain becomes mad or a poet'.

The North and North-East were particularly badly hit with all roads into Newcastle blocked for several hours. Drifts in places were twenty feet deep and around 1,500 cars and several hundred lorries were abandoned. In Consett, County Durham, a tea-break nearly turned into a disaster when the cabin in which six workmen at the British Steel plant were taking their break collapsed under the weight of snow. Colleagues dug them out and all were taken to hospital. Astonishingly, one of two men who died in the blizzards had gone out 'without a coat and wearing only light shoes'. James Mitchell, 42, from Todmorden in Yorkshire collapsed and died in the snow only yards from the caravan where he lived. The other victim, Alfred Cross, also forty-two and 'a keen walker', was found dead at the side of the Snake Pass on the A57 between Sheffield and Manchester. Twenty motorists may not have been too distraught to be snowed in the Jolly Sailor pub at Moorsholme, North Yorkshire, for the entire weekend. One of them, a lorry driver, John Clarkson, cheerfully reported that they were 'short of bread and milk, but not beer'. He and his companions may have been even more pleased that the snowploughs did not reach the pub until too late for them to get to work on Monday morning, but motorists in Cleveland were less happy to discover, when returning to the cars they had abandoned during the blizzard, that others had been there first. A police spokesman revealed that one car had all four wheels removed and another's headlights had been pinched.

The weather turned even worse the next day in the North, with police telling motorists not to drive into blizzard-hit Northumberland and Cumbria, and there was 'virtually no access to Scotland' at all. Police advised motorists and particularly lorry-drivers to stay in Newcastle for the night, rather than try to drive North, because 'they just won't get through'.

By 26 March the traditional North-South divide was once more in evidence with South-East England basking in temperatures of 15°C, the warmest day of the year so far, while torrential rain, and blizzards of sleet and snow were still sweeping the North. It was the last flurry of the coldest winter since 1963, but 1979 - "The Winter of Discontent" - had one final sting in its tail. In the General Election on 4 May 1979 Margaret Thatcher swept to power on a platform that included a pledge to curb the power of the unions. It seemed as if neither winters, nor the political landscape of Britain would ever be the same again, but while the iron lady's political legacy still lingers – albeit a little tinged with rust – ice, snow, burst pipes and traffic chaos seems to have become a regular part of the midwinter landscape once more.

EPITAPH

How Often Will It Happen Again?

Following a run of very mild winters over the past couple of decades, it perhaps came as a surprise to many when Arctic and Siberian weather staged a dramatic return during the last few winters bringing much of the country to a standstill. Only a few years before a prominent UK scientist even commented that snow would become increasingly rare in coming years, so much so that children might never see a harsh winter again. But Mother Nature never fails to surprise.

One of the central themes of climate projections, based on increases in greenhouse gases, is that winters in this country will become milder and wetter. Over the last 20 years or so it seemed that these projections were coming true; some winters even across higher parts of Britain saw very little snow, with Autumn lasting longer and Spring beginning earlier. Winter, it would seem, was getting squeezed and the seasons felt at times as though they were starting to merge.

We had become complacent; gone were the snow chains that in the 60's and 70's were a common feature in the boot of my dad's car as he travelled over the Pennines. Gone were the two sledges that as a young child I used every winter without fail. And gone were the large stores of rock salt that councils bought in as a matter of course every summer in anticipation of a 'normal' cold winter.

The answer as to why we have suddenly lurched into winters of such ferocity could lie with the behaviour of the sun, an old fashioned branch of forecasting which, in the days of expensive multi-million pound computers that we have now, seems to have been largely forgotten by most, but not all, forecasting organisations.

The sun goes in cycles, the most common of which is an 11 year cycle; less common is a rather grandly named 'bi-centennial' cycle. These cycles are in fact highs and lows of activity on the sun. In the last few years, the sun has been behaving very oddly, similar in many ways to the way it behaved in the late 1700s. What followed, in the early 1800s was the Dalton solar minima, named after the meteorologist John Dalton.

In research published early in 2009, Australian scientist David Archibald studied the Dalton Minima of the early 1800s to see if there were any changes in weather conditions at the same time. The results were clear. Temperatures at our latitudes fell over the period by as much as 2 degrees Celsius. Those of you who are keen on British history or literature may make the link: it was Dickensian Britain, a time of cold and snowy winters.

Archibald concluded that it was likely that the solar cycle in the coming years would be similar to that of the early 1800s, and that average temperatures were about to fall as a result; winters at our latitudes were about to get much, much colder. His findings were based in large part on the Central England Temperature dataset, with records going back to 1659 that do indeed show a sustained drop during the early part of the 1800s.

Although Archibald's conclusions came as a surprise to some, the idea that the sun can influence our climate is nothing new. In fact Professor Lamb, a well-respected former climatologist from the University of East Anglia, conducted detailed research into the solar cycle and its possible influence on our weather. One of his papers shows clear empirical evidence that at times of solar minima, more often than not, pressure is higher across Greenland and Iceland. This would cause the jet stream, a narrow ribbon of very high winds high up in the atmosphere which usually brings us mild and wet weather from the Atlantic, to assume a more southerly position than normal across Southern Europe, in turn causing cold easterly winds to be dragged across the UK from Russia.

The mechanism for this solar/climate interaction was poorly understood back in the 1960's, and little progress seems to have been made today. But there can be no doubt that the sun has a dominant role to play in the climate patterns we experience here on the ground – and has played a dominant role in the past.

The most famous of the sun's inactive periods in the past came in the 1600s and was called the 'Maunder' solar minima after research conducted by English astronomer Walter Maunder. This was a period of very cold winters across the UK and Europe, named the 'little ice age'. such was its ferocity. It coincided with years of very low solar activity captured by astronomers at the time, by the annual number of sun spots which for decades was zero.

Another interesting twist to this story comes from Russia. During Glasnost in the 1990s, many thousands of documents which had previously been kept secret by the Soviet authorities were released into the public domain. And it was clear from reading some of these, what Russian scientists thought about where global climate was heading – and it wasn't heading warmer.

Similar research was conducted by Dr Abdussamatov, head of the space research laboratory in Russia. He focused on the little known 'bicentennial cycle', which as the name suggests has an approximate cycle lasting 200 years. What he demonstrated was that the previous low point of solar activity in this cycle coincided with the Maunder minima through the mid 1600s and early 1700s; what followed was a gradual increase in activity which reached a peak during the 1900s; and now as we head through the early stages of the 21st century, activity, based on this bi-centennial cycle, is once more decreasing. His conclusion is also clear; the sun's gradual drop in activity over the coming decades is likely to outweigh any warming that may result due to manmade global warming.

Many scientists don't follow this line of thinking, although the idea that the sun could have been responsible for the last few years' cold winters, having been mostly overlooked by mainstream science for many years, recently got a boost from Professor Lockwood at Reading University.

Professor Lockwood conducted similar research to that which David Archibald published a year earlier. He compared solar activity with the Central England Temperature dataset and came to a similar conclusion. The prolonged solar minima could indeed have caused the bitter winters that we have just experienced, and moreover, it could be a taste of things to come.

But he did point out that the unusual solar cycle has merely re-distributed global warmth by disrupting climate patterns, and that at a time of record cold across parts of Europe, other areas, such as Northern Canada and Alaska, together with Arctic areas were experiencing abnormal warmth.

The intense cold of the last few winters also reminded us of how reliant the UK is on the Gulf Stream to keep our country mild. In fact the only reason why our winters are usually mild and wet is because of a large current of warm water that flows past us from the Gulf of Mexico. If it were not for this, our climate would be much colder, bearing in mind that we are positioned on the same latitude as Canada.

If climate projections are to be believed and global temperatures warm in the coming decades, there is a risk, albeit a small one, that the Gulf Stream could be disrupted by a warming planet. In fact this scenario has been highlighted by the Met Office Hadley centre as one of the possible consequences of climate change. The theory is quite simple. A warmer planet would lead to large scale melting of ice, with huge quantities of fresh water pouring into the Atlantic Ocean. This would act to reduce the salinity and density of sea water, which is critical to the strength of the Gulf Stream current. One of the worst case scenarios shows the Gulf current becoming disrupted and 'cut off' in mid Atlantic, plunging the UK into much colder winters which would be more typical of a country at latitudes similar to Canada.

Some computer simulations show that the UK's annual temperature could cool by up to 5 degrees Celsius in a relatively short period of time of 10-20 years. But extremes would be far worse than this. Daily minimum temperatures in Central England could regularly fall well below minus 10C. If this were to happen, disruption to society would be enormous with agriculture, transport and other infrastructure severely hit.

All this is nothing new. At the end of the last Ice Age, when the ice sheet covering North America melted, the sudden increase in fresh water reduced the salinity of the north Atlantic and therefore less 'dense water' sank and moved towards the equator. This reduced, or even shut down completely, the warm Gulf Stream. Temperatures in north-west Europe fell by 5C in just a few decades.

Recent observations have shown that since 1950 there has been a decrease of 20% in the flow of cold water in the Faeroe Bank channel between Greenland and Scotland. This is one source of cold dense water that drives the density-based component of the Gulf Stream. There may be an increase in flow from other cold water sources, but, if not, it could be the start of the slowdown of the Gulf Stream.

The Intergovernmental Panel on Climate Change believe it is very likely that the Gulf Stream will slow down during the 21st Century but very unlikely it will undergo a 'large abrupt transition'. The average reduction predicted by the various models used is 25%. This slowing will have a cooling effect but the temperature will still increase in the region overall.

Following speculation that a slowing of the Gulf Stream could have been responsible for the cold winter of 2009/2010, the Met Office issued a statement saying that there was no evidence that this was happening. Indeed a report released at the Cancun climate change conference stated that improved observations cast doubt on previously reported evidence of a recent slowdown in the Gulf Stream which keeps northern Europe warmer than it would otherwise be.

Climate scientist Mark Maslin, of University College London, agreed, also claiming that there was no evidence to suggest that a slow-down in the Gulf Stream was to blame for

Europe's cold winter, adding that it was an atmospheric effect and not due to a slow-down of ocean circulation.

But the message is clear. We can't as easily dismiss the real possibility that the sun's unusual behaviour is to blame for a return of harsh wintry weather in the last few years. And there has to be a good chance that rather than the last few winters being a blip in a period of increasingly mild and wet winters, we need to prepare ourselves for more cold winter in the years to come. It's unlikely that every winter will be severe, but if the solar cycle is affecting our climate and jet stream like some scientists believe, then the UK needs to get used to scenes like we witnessed last winter that many thought had been confined to the climate history books for ever.

Paul Hudson

Acknowledgements

Many individuals and organisations helped us in the preparation of this book. At Great Northern Books, our grateful thanks to Barry Cox, Patricia Lennon, David Joy and David Burrill; to David Barnett, Features Editor at the Telegraph & Argus, Bradford; and to Mike Baker; David Bailey-Bristol; Malcolm Beaton; Rod Bowen; Shaun Carroll; Hugh Conway-Jones; John Cundall; Marian and Peter Down; Aneurin Evans; David Fisher; Alan George; David Gott; Geoff Kirby; Geoff Matsell; Ian Mean; David Nicholson; Ed Perkins; Helen Reynolds; Robert Thomas; Ken Tytherleigh; David Wakeley; and Anne Wood.